G000149837

# INDUSTRIAL ARCHAEOLOGY of SURREY

Ta25 Outwood windmills, c1930

*Photo: Roger Packham Collection*

## THE INDUSTRIES OF SURREY
*by Eric Wood*

Surrey is an unusual county. Between 1889 and 1974 it lost about a fifth of its area, and much of its population, to London; but what is left retains a surprising amount of character. Although its history, population and atmosphere have been deeply influenced, indeed severely distorted, by its proximity to the capital (and even though its county administration is in the London Borough of Kingston-upon-Thames), yet it is still a vigorous and individual county like any other. The extent of modern Surrey, its administrative districts and principal towns, are shown opposite.

The London influence was at first, and has to some extent remained, a romantic one. By the end of the 18th century the London middle classes were spending holidays in the Surrey hills, and soon were building villas there. Artists and writers came too, and publicised the untamed countryside in paintings, poems and novels. By the late 19th century, and further stimulated by the railways, Surrey had become thickly dotted with villas, and the towns were spreading fast. Yet beneath this veneer of picturesque suburbanisation the rural heart of the county still beats – and can, particularly south of the Downs, still be felt. And this heart is not only bucolic, but contains an unexpectedly strong industrial base.

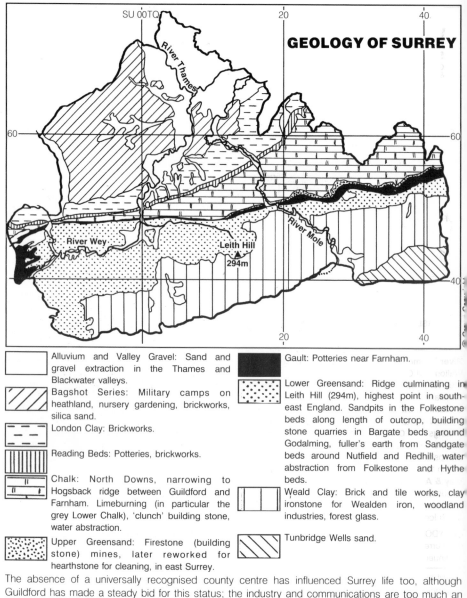

**GEOLOGY OF SURREY**

SU 00TQ    20    40

60 — — 60

River Wey · Leith Hill ▲ 294m

River Thames

River Mole

20    40

40

Alluvium and Valley Gravel: Sand and gravel extraction in the Thames and Blackwater valleys.

Bagshot Series: Military camps on heathland, nursery gardening, brickworks, silica sand.

London Clay: Brickworks.

Reading Beds: Potteries, brickworks.

Chalk: North Downs, narrowing to Hogsback ridge between Guildford and Farnham. Limeburning (in particular the grey Lower Chalk), 'clunch' building stone, water abstraction.

Upper Greensand: Firestone (building stone) mines, later reworked for hearthstone for cleaning, in east Surrey.

Gault: Potteries near Farnham.

Lower Greensand: Ridge culminating in Leith Hill (294m), highest point in south-east England. Sandpits in the Folkestone beds along length of outcrop, building stone quarries in Bargate beds around Godalming, fuller's earth from Sandgate beds around Nutfield and Redhill, water abstraction from Folkestone and Hythe beds.

Weald Clay: Brick and tile works, clay ironstone for Wealden iron, woodland industries, forest glass.

Tunbridge Wells sand.

The absence of a universally recognised county centre has influenced Surrey life too, although Guildford has made a steady bid for this status; the industry and communications are too much an extension of London (and London has swallowed and digested much industry and life which was once undeniably Surrey's, such as those in Southwark and the Wandle valley). Yet to say that Surrey is more an attitude than a county is not only inaccurate, but patronising and unfair.

Before we look at the industries, the geological map on the next page will throw further light on the county. Surrey falls into two halves: that north of the chalk Downs, with soils of the London basin and the acid Bagshot sands; and the richer land south of the Downs, taking in the greensands and **2** gault and entering the claylands of the Weald. Much of this land is poor, either acid and thin or heavy and wooded; agriculture in Surrey has never been easy, which is of course one reason for the colonisation of the county by suburban homes. This is also shown by the paucity of castles

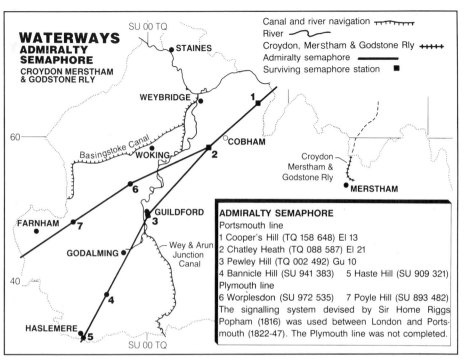

WATERWAYS
ADMIRALTY
SEMAPHORE
CROYDON MERSTHAM
& GODSTONE RLY

Canal and river navigation ⊤⊤⊤⊤⊤⊤⊤
River
Croydon, Merstham & Godstone Rly ╫╫╫╫
Admiralty semaphore ▬▬▬▬▬
Surviving semaphore station ■

ADMIRALTY SEMAPHORE
Portsmouth line
1 Cooper's Hill (TQ 158 648) El 13
2 Chatley Heath (TQ 088 587) El 21
3 Pewley Hill (TQ 002 492) Gu 10
4 Bannicle Hill (SU 941 383)    5 Haste Hill (SU 909 321)
Plymouth line
6 Worplesdon (SU 972 535)    7 Poyle Hill (SU 893 482)
The signalling system devised by Sir Home Riggs Popham (1816) was used between London and Portsmouth (1822-47). The Plymouth line was not completed.

**River Thames**: Navigable throughout medieval period. Thames Commissioners established 1770 made cuts at Walton and Chertsey. Pound locks built on Surrey section 1811-18.
**Wey Navigation**: Act 1651. Opened from Weybridge to Guildford 1653. 22 km, 12 locks. National Trust 1964 –. Regular commercial traffic to Guildford until 1958 and to Coxe's lock, Weybridge until 1969.
**Godalming Navigation**: Wey Navigation Act 1760. Completed from Guildford to Godalming 1763. 7 km, 4 locks. National Trust 1968 -. Regular commercial traffic to Godalming until 1925, to Stonebridge until 1950.
**Basingstoke Canal**: Act 1788. Opened to Basingstoke 1796. 25.5 km, 28 locks in Surrey; 33.5 km, 1 lock, 2 tunnels in Hampshire. Commercial traffic to Basingstoke ceased 1901, to Woking 1949. The Surrey & Hampshire Canal Society was formed in 1966. The canal was purchased by the two County Councils in 1973 and in 1990 restoration is nearing completion.
**Wey & Arun Junction Canal**: Act 1813. Opened 1816, closed 1871. 17.5 km, 15 locks in Surrey; 12 km, 8 locks in Sussex. The Wey & Arun Canal Society (1970) and Trust (1973) were formed to campaign for the eventual reopening of the canal. Several features have been restored and much of the towpath is designated the Wey South long-distance footpath.
**CROYDON, MERSTHAM & GODSTONE RAILWAY** Plateway for horse-drawn waggons, built as an extension to the Surrey Iron Railway (1803) from Wandsworth to Croydon. Act 1803. Opened to Merstham 1805 but not continued further. Closed 1838.

(Farnham, Guildford, Reigate, Blechingley and few others), and of great houses, and the total absence of really major ones - Clandon and Sutton Place come nearest, but are still relatively small, although of high quality; the royal palace of Nonsuch no longer exists. Equally, there are few churches of distinction. Yet look beyond the partly rural, partly suburban face, and the rich and vigorous industrial aspect appears.
The industries of Surrey fall into two broad categories: the old rural industries, which survive from medieval and sometimes even Roman times, even if some have died out on the way; and those of less local flavour, which accompanied the 19th century development of the county and its urban growth.
The traditional industries of Surrey are those which used the local materials. Continental influence was strong, for example in the early glass industry, in which immigrants from Normandy and

3

Wa07 Drying and bleaching grounds, Westbrook leather mill, Godalming, early 20th century.

Lorraine played a major part. Glass was made in a few parishes around Chiddingfold (and extending into Sussex), using local sand, stone and clay, and oak and coppice-wood for potash and firing the furnaces. The earliest dated glasshouse was at Blunden's Wood, Hambledon (c1330), but some glass might have been made earlier. The industry passed through two main phases, the second beginning in the 1560s, and by the 1610s had moved away from the Weald. Remains of a glasshouse of the 1550s can be seen in Sidney Wood, Alfold. The other major Wealden industry was iron, made in Sussex from prehistoric and Roman times until 1828, Surrey being very much on the fringe. The ore was mainly clay ironstone, but other ferruginous rocks were also used; firing was by charcoal. Bloomery sites are known from Godstone, Leigh, Lingfield and Thursley. Some dozen water-powered sites are recorded in Surrey, including Thursley, Witley, West End, Haslemere (Imbhams), Burningfold, Abinger Hammer, Coneyhurst, Vachery, Ewood, Leigh and Woodcock. Some of these are furnace sites, others forges, and traces of bays, water-systems and working areas survive. Ore was mined in pits, eg at Hambledon.

Pottery was made in Roman times on a large scale in Alice Holt Forest, just over the Hampshire border south-west of Farnham, and a few kilns of this complex have been found in Surrey. The Surrey White Wares of the 13-15th centuries were made from a band of white clay running from Farnham to Ewell and Cheam. Earthenwares and terracottas are still made at Wrecclesham (and were made for a time at Compton). Tiles were made at Ashtead by the Romans, at Farnham in medieval times, and famous inlaid medieval tiles were made at Chertsey. Woodland crafts—fencing, besoms, walking sticks—are still carried on in the Wealden fringe, and charcoal burning was ubiquitous in the forests. There are sawmills at Guildford, and for example on the Albury estate. Leather was centred at Godalming (as well as Bermondsey and Southwark in the old county). Cloth was made on a large scale at Guildford (where Racks Close is a reminder), Farnham and Godalming, with knitwear at the latter also. Gunpowder was made at Tolworth, Ewell and Chilworth, from the 16th century to the 20th. There are extensive remains of the works at Chilworth, and factory housing in the village.

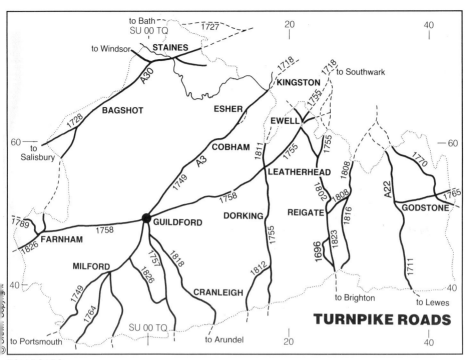

TURNPIKE ROADS

**TOLLROADS**
The earliest toll road was authorised from Crawley to Reigate in 1696 though not improved for carriages until 1755. The Portsmouth Road (modern A3) was turnpiked in 1711 from Portsmouth to Petersfield in Hampshire, in 1718 from Southwark to Kingston and in 1749 from Kingston to Petersfield. Several other roads were turnpiked around 1750 and 1810, the last from Godalming to near Dunsfold in 1826.

**SURREY TURNPIKES**
Corresponding modern roads (many altered from the 1930s onwards) are indicated by route numbers. Diversions are shown at Esher (around Claremont House c.1768) and at Reigate (road tunnel 1823).

**EARLY ROADS AND TRACKWAYS**
North Downs Trackway: An early route along the foot of the chalk escarpment, romantically named the 'Pilgrims' Way' in the 19th century. Roman: Four routes radiating from London pass through Surrey: London to Silchester via Staines (the modern A30); London to Chichester via Ewell and Dorking (partly the ·A29, partly green lanes and footpaths); London towards Brighton (approximately the A22); London towards Lewes (approximately following the east county boundary).

Medieval: The Gough map (14th century) provides evidence for the following: London - Kingston - Guildford - Farnham - Winchester and Exeter; London - Brentford - Colnbrook - Bath; London - Dorking - Horsham and Shoreham; London - Chiddingfold - Petworth and Arundel.

Tudor and Stuart: From 1584, ironmasters were required to provide cartloads of roadmetal in proportion to loads carried in the Weald in winter.

---

Large-scale fishponds survive at Frensham; dovecotes at many places — that at Albury has recently been restored. Fruit and hops were grown extensively, the latter on a large scale around Farnham, which has imposing maltings. Local breweries were widespread, and there are important coaching inns at for example Dorking, Ripley, Guildford and Farnham. Windmills survive in a few places, the postmill at Outwood being distinguished; the Lowfield Heath windmill is being rebuilt. Watermills were frequent on the Surrey rivers, and were used for a variety of purposes — and many changed their use during their lives. The main uses included corn-milling (eg Haxted and Shalford), fulling (Guildford and Godalming), silk (Thursley) and paper, eg on the Tillingbourne at Chilworth and on the Wey at Catteshall and Haslemere. **5**

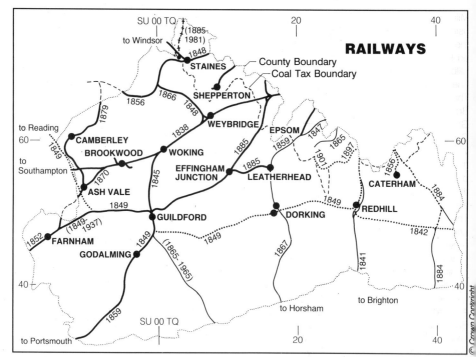

SU 00 TQ    20      40

to Windsor (1885-1981)

**RAILWAYS**

1848
STAINES

—— County Boundary
········ Coal Tax Boundary

1856   1866   SHEPPERTON

1848
1879   WEYBRIDGE

to Reading
60—
CAMBERLEY   1838   EPSOM   1847
1849   BROOKWOOD   WOKING   1859   1865   1897   —60
to
Southampton   1870   EFFINGHAM   1885   1901   1856
  JUNCTION   1845   LEATHERHEAD
ASH VALE   CATERHAM   1884
1849   1849
GUILDFORD   DORKING   REDHILL
1849-1937   1849   1842
1852   FARNHAM   1849
GODALMING   1865-1965   1867   1841   1884

40 —   1859   to Brighton   —40
SU 00 TQ   to Horsham
to Portsmouth    20      40

© Crown Copyright

**KEY TO MAP**

➤ London & South Western Railway (LSWR)   ⌒⌒ London Brighton & South Coast Railway (LBSCR)
········ South Eastern Railway (SER)   +++ Great Western Railway (GWR)
– – – – City of London Coal and Wine Duty Boundary (1861)   *Dates in brackets indicate closed lines.*
**COAL TAX POSTS**
The London Coal and Wine Duties (Continuance) Act of 1861 redefined the boundary, corresponding to that of the Metropolitan Police District, at which duty was payable on goods entering London.
Posts, large numbers of which survive, were erected on transport routes. Most were newly cast, to the standard design illustrated opposite, (approximately 1.2m high), by Henry Grissell of the Regent's Canal Ironworks. Some earlier markers were relocated and some were set up later. Types include short and tall iron and stone obelisks and cast iron plates.

The extractive industries were always important in Surrey, as indicated on page 2. The influence of London is seen in the reservoirs for the capital's water supply which dominate the landscape in parts of Spelthorne and Elmbridge. With a relatively high population since the 18th century, and with the closeness of London, transport is well to the fore. Maps showing the main turnpike roads, waterways and railways are given in this introductory section. There is a fine series of medieval bridges over the Wey, built by Waverley Abbey, for example at Tilford and Eashing. Features associated with waterways include the treadwheel crane at Guildford, which probably dates from the late 17th century, the riverside warehouses at Guildford and the fine agent's house of the Wey & Arun Canal (1816) in Sidney Wood near Alfold. Restoration of the Basingstoke Canal (1796) is nearing completion. Much of the dense network of railways out of London ran through Surrey and Woking is partly a railway creation. Several early stations remain, for example the restored redundant station at Baynards, and other details such as the embankment and its excavated pond at Weybridge. A rare Surrey distinction is the Surrey Iron Railway (1803) and its extension the **6** Croydon, Merstham & Godstone Railway, the course of which can still be traced. The SIR was the earliest public railway in Britain.

Military works are represented by the systems of naval signal stations, using shutters from 1796 to 1814 and semaphores from the 1820s to 1847; the series of fortified storehouses (1895-7) along the Downs, of which that on Pewley Hill, Guildford is a good example; and the Second World War pillboxes and tank obstacles.

There is a wide variety of modern industries, from the statue foundry at Thames Ditton to the world's first motor testing and racing circuit at Brooklands (1906), Lagonda cars at Egham, Dennis fire-engines at Guildford; aircraft works at Weybridge and Dunsfold (the early airport at Croydon is no longer in Surrey); Plessey at Addlestone; Unwins' at Woking; and many more. Miscellaneous items include street furniture and the fine raised pavements at Dorking and Haslemere; the Wine and Coal posts on the perimeter of the Metropolitan Police District; water towers; the Catteshall water turbine. Godalming was the first town to be lit by electricity (1881).

The past decade has seen the start of a quiet revolution in the character and location of industry in Surrey. The completion of the M25 and the growth of traffic density at the country's two major air terminals have elevated industrial property prices (and now rates) to a level where the traditional mix of small and medium size firms of a very varied nature is rapidly giving way to high value-added, high technology young companies grouped strategically in purpose-built business or technology estates. A good example is the University of Surrey's Research Park at Guildford. But in view of the amount of service industry in Surrey, the very low unemployment, and the considerable areas of Green Belt land, the County Council wish to control and restrict industrial development and associated housing, and make the best use of existing land resources.

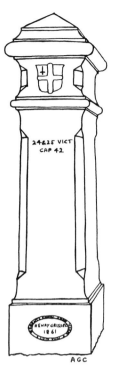

Coal tax post

# GAZETTEER

The following gazetteer is divided into sections corresponding to the administrative districts of modern Surrey, with sites arranged by location. It is intended primarily as a field guide but a few private sites and industries with no visible remains have been included because of their importance in the industrial history of the area. Every effort has been made to provide accurate information. However much redevelopment is in progress and some details may soon become out-of-date. Care should be taken to avoid intrusion on private land and to ensure personal safety. In the case of underground sites, enquiries may be made to Subterranea Britannica, c/o 96a Brighton Road, South Croydon CR2 6AD.

## KEY TO GAZETTEER SYMBOLS

| | |
|---|---|
| **SC** | Scheduled Ancient Monument |
| **LSI LSII★ LSII** | Listed Building, indicating grade I, II★ and II |
| **CA** | Conservation Area |
| **NT** | National Trust property |
| ✳ | Sites which can be seen from a public place |
| ❏ | Sites open to the public, including museums open at fixed hours / seasons and shops etc open for trading |
| ■ | Sites which are not open to the public |

7

The Borough of Elmbridge contains the towns of Cobham, Esher, Walton and Weybridge. The River Thames forms its northern boundary and is joined by the Wey at Weybridge and the Mole at East Molesey. Features relating to transport and communications include Thames bridges, fine examples of milestones on the Portsmouth road between Esher and Cobham, Admiralty semaphore towers and some 25 surviving City of London coal tax posts.

The influence of London is particularly apparent in the huge storage reservoirs which cater for the capital's water supply. The various water companies involved were formed in the latter half of the 19th century but most of the reservoirs date from the early years of this century and one, the Queen Elizabeth II Reservoir, from 1962.

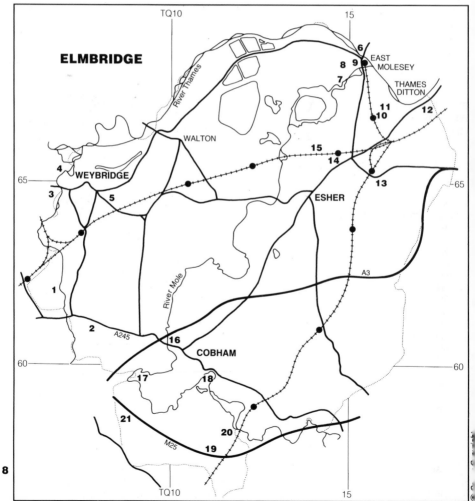

Another influence emanating from London has been the building of residences by the wealthy and influential, following the pattern set by the royal palace of Hampton Court on the opposite bank of the Thames. Two estates are worthy of note: Claremont at Esher, owned by the Dukes of Newcastle, and Painshill Park at Cobham, landscaped by Charles Hamilton in the late 18th century. This is being restored to its original condition, complete with a large waterwheel by Bramah & Son. Another major project is the creation of a museum at the pioneer motor-racing and aviation centre of Brooklands which became the nucleus of the aircraft industry around Weybridge.

Early water-powered industries, including corn milling, paper, gunpowder, brass wire and battery, iron forging and oil seed crushing, were carried on at various sites on the Wey and Mole, most of which have been redeveloped. In the 18th and early 19th centuries the iron masters Alexander Raby, John Hitchcock and others were active at several sites. However shallow trenches at St George's Hill [e.g. TQ 077 637], interpreted as iron workings, are now considered pre-medieval and probably iron age.

Two more recent industries which have vanished, leaving only the legacy of their products, are the film studios at Walton on Thames started by Cecil Hepworth in 1899, which survived into the mid 1960s, and the bronze statue foundry in Summer Road, Thames Ditton [TQ 15 67], active from 1874 to 1940 and demolished in 1972. A gantry crane (1874) which spanned the production area of the works was saved by SIHG and is being restored at the Old Kiln Museum, Tilford (Wa 17). The foundry produced many celebrated monuments including the massive 'Peace' Quadriga above the Wellington Arch on Constitution Hill, London. Examples of its work in the Borough include the War Memorial in St Nicholas Church, Thames Ditton [TQ 161 673] and the inscribed scroll on the gravestone in the churchyard to Alfred Morrison, foreman moulder at the foundry, who died in 1924.

## EI 01 BROOKLANDS MUSEUM, WEYBRIDGE

TQ 072 620  **CA**  ❏

The world's first banked motor racing circuit, built in 1906-7 on the initiative of Hugh Fortescue Locke King. Originally envisaged as a track for testing production cars when roads had a 20 mph speed limit, it became a focus for national and international racing and test driving up to the Second World War, when the concrete track was camouflaged with earth and trees.

Brooklands also became a pioneer aviation centre when A V Roe succeeded in becoming airborne over the finishing straight in 1908. It was associated with the Sopwith, Avro, Vickers and Martinsyde aircraft companies, became the manufacturing base of Vickers-Armstrong before and during the Second World War, and later became the headquarters of the British Aircraft Corporation.

In the 1980s, British Aerospace concentrated its work at other sites, including the former Hawker-Siddeley works at Kingston. In 1984 Gallaghers purchased 40 acres at Brooklands and set aside 30 acres for a museum. This is being developed by Elmbridge Borough Council and other bodies. It includes the Clubhouse **LSII**, Members' Restaurant, Barnes Wallis's office and a restored section of motor racing track **SC**. It also holds the Second World War Vickers Wellington bomber salvaged from Loch Ness in 1985.

EI01 Mountain Championship, Brooklands, 1937
*Photo: Chris Shepheard Collection*

## EI 02 COBHAM BUS MUSEUM

TQ 079 611  ❏ *(summer)*

Collection of the London Bus Preservation Trust, housed in a garage on the corner of Byfleet Road and Redhill Road.

A circular **cast iron kiosk** in Byfleet Road originally housed a transformer to boost the voltage at the end of a long supply feed. Manufactured c1900-1910 by the British Electrical Transformer Company, Hayes, Middlesex. It probably incorporated a street lamp.

## EI03 WEYBRIDGE BRIDGE

TQ 068 647 **LSII** ✳

The present three-arched bridge (1865) has steel girders on brick and stone faced piers and abutments, and cast iron balustrades. It is bypassed by a road and bridge begun in 1939 and finished after the Second World War.

## EI04 THAMES LOCK AND WEYBRIDGE MILL

TQ 073 655 ✳

On the Wey Navigation (**NT** ☐) near its junction with the Thames. The original lock keeper's cottage still stands. Weybridge or Ham Haw Mill was built on the navigation in 1691 as a paper mill. It was an iron mill by 1720 to 1817 and was depicted on a trade token issued by the ironmaster John Bunn in 1812. It was an oil seed mill from 1842 to 1963 when it burned down. The site has remained in industrial use and is due for redevelopment.

## EI05 CINEMA, QUEEN'S ROAD, WEYBRIDGE

TQ 083 645 ☐

An Odeon cinema built in 1934, now the Roman Catholic church of St Martin de Porres.

## EI06 HAMPTON COURT BRIDGE

TQ 154 685 **LSII CA** ✳

Ferro-concrete with brick and stone facings in three arches, designed by Sir Edwin Lutyens and opened in 1933. Hampton Court Way (A309) was constructed to link the new bridge with the Portsmouth Road near Esher. This involved building a new bridge over the River Ember [TQ 154 682] (**LSII**). Also by Lutyens, in the same style as the main bridge.

## EI07 FORMER TELEPHONE BOX, EAST MOLESEY

TQ 148 679 **CA** ✳

An unusual small kiosk-like building, which juts out from the front window of 44 Walton Road, was the first public telephone call box in the district, opened October 1900.

## EI08 LOWER MILL (STERTE MILL), EAST MOLESEY

TQ 153 682 ✳

Lower and Upper mills were recorded at East Molesey in 1251. Both produced gunpowder during the Commonwealth but the Lower Mill then reverted to corn milling. The present brick building dates from the 1820s. This was used as a corn mill, a saw mill, a factory for 'Zenith' motor cycles and a tent works, before being converted to modern offices.

Gunpowder manufacture continued at the Upper Mill [TQ 144 676] until c1780 when the site was incorporated into East Molesey Park. The associated islands and weirs now form part of the gardens of a sports club.

## EI09 ELECTRICITY SUB-STATION, EAST MOLESEY

TQ 153 684 **CA** ✳

A corrugated iron building in Feltham Avenue was originally the Trinity Church at New Malden. It was moved to its present site in 1882 for use as a public hall and later became an electricity substation and workshop.

## EI10 THE OLD SLAUGHTER HOUSE, THAMES DITTON

TQ 160 669 **LSII CA** ☐

A 17th century timber building in the High Street, now a picture gallery.

## EI11 FERRY WORKS, THAMES DITTON

TQ 161 673 **CA** ✳

Outstanding architectural conversion for modern business use. Built by the engineers Willand & Robinson in 1879 and much rebuilt after a fire in 1888. The 1888 rebuild is the earliest known example of a 'saw-tooth' north light roof in a machine shop. The firm moved to Rugby in 1911 and was absorbed by English Electric. The premises were taken over by Messrs Auto Carriers, makers of AC cars. After the Second World War they made fibreglass 3-wheeled invalid cars for the Ministry of Pensions, and the 'Petite', a private car based on the same design.

EI11 Ferry Works, Thames Ditton   *Photo: G M Crocker*

## EI12 WATERWORKS, LONG DITTON

TQ 172 673 ✳

Opened in 1852 by the Lambeth Water Company when it moved its intake upstream. The Metropolitan Water Act of that year prohibited the extraction of water for household use below Teddington Weir and the Chelsea Water Company also moved to Long Ditton. The two companies were incorporated into the Metropolitan Water Board in 1903. The works contracted during subsequent rationalisation and the change from steam to electric power.

### EI13 COOPER'S HILL SEMAPHORE TOWER

TQ 158 648 **LSII**  &#42;

On Telegraph Hill at Hinchley Wood, a three-storey brick building, externally stuccoed, now a private house. One of the chain of Admiralty semaphore stations in use 1822-47.

### EI14 TURNPIKE OBELISK, ESHER

TQ 147 656 **LSII★**  &#42;

A cylinder of limestone known as the 'White Lady', outside the Orleans Arms in Portsmouth Road. It stands about 2.5m high and has a ball finial bearing the date 1767 and three panels of places and distances.
Milestones on the old Portsmouth Road and Claremont diversion include a fine example in Blackhills estate [TQ 134 630] (**SC, LSII★ ✻**).

### EI15 COAL TAX POSTS, ESHER

TQ 140 658  &#42;

A 1m cast iron post in Lower Green Road and a 4.3m granite obelisk on the railway embankment by 100 Douglas Road are on opposite sides of the railway near a footpath under the line.

### EI16 COBHAM BRIDGE

TQ 099 605 **LSII**  &#42;

Brick, nine-arch bridge by George Gwilt carrying the old A3 over the River Mole, widened in 1914.

### EI17 PAINSHILL PARK WATER WHEEL

TQ 090 599 **LSII**  ☐

The late 18th century landscaped park of Painshill, laid out by Charles Hamilton, is being restorated by the Painshill Park Trust. The 30 ft (9m) diameter cast iron water wheel, made by Bramah & Son in the 1830s to operate a pump for an ornamental lake, was restored in 1988. An earlier water wheel, known from documentary sources, had four leather tubes curved from the rim to the axis which scooped up water and delivered it to a trough at the centre of the wheel. A horse driven pump for the 'Roman Bath House' [TQ 095 601] has also been restored.

### EI18 COBHAM MILL

TQ 112 599 **LSII, CA**  &#42;

Brick building with tiled gables of c1820. It was one of two mills with water wheels between, the older of which was demolished for road straightening in 1951. Corn milling ceased in the 1920s. The waterwheels are derelict but much of the machinery survives.

### EI19 TINMAN'S ROW, DOWNSIDE, COBHAM

TQ 112 580 **LSII, CA**  &#42;

Cottages of domestic tinplate workers connected with Alexander Raby's ironworks at Downside Mill. The nearby water pump of 1858 (✻) was supplied from the River Mole by a small waterwheel (by Whitmore & Binyon of Wickham Market, Suffolk) at TQ 114 588 (✻), which also pumped water to Cobham Park.

### EI20 DOWNSIDE MILL, COBHAM

TQ 118 583  ■

A medieval corn mill, a paper mill from the late 17th century, an iron mill occupied by Alexander Raby by 1773 to c1810 and a flock mill by 1825. There are remains of a breastshot waterwheel and associated gearing, and iron slag occurs in the vicinity.

### EI21 CHATLEY HEATH SEMAPHORE TOWER

TQ 088 587 **SC, LSII**  ☐

Red brick, 18m high octagonal tower of five storeys, erected as an Admiralty signalling station at the junction of lines from London to Portsmouth and Plymouth and active 1822-47. The tower was occupied as a house until the 1960s and then became derelict. It was restored in 1989, complete with signalling gear, by the Surrey Historic Buildings Trust and Surrey County Council.

EI21 Chatley Heath semaphore tower; Official Opening, July 1989   *Photo: G M Crocker*

**11**

Epsom owes its origin as a town to the discovery of a medicinal spring on the common in the early 17th century. A new well was opened in the town at the end of the century. Epsom was the first fashionable spa resort in Britain and reached the height of its popularity between 1690 and 1727, particularly through the enterprise of the apothecary Livingstone. The quantity of water from the two wells was not however sufficient for the manufacture of Epsom Salts (hydrated magnesium sulphate) on any scale, and these were produced commercially elsewhere in the London area, in particular at Acton and Shooter's Hill. Epsom spa was eclipsed by other resort towns during the 18th century.

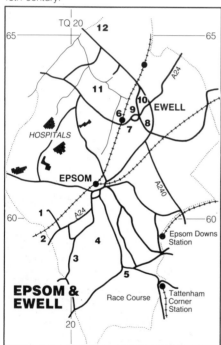

The local Downs were used for horse racing by the time of Elizabeth I. Epsom became a popular racing centre with the introduction of the Oaks race in 1779, named after the Earl of Derby's residence, and the Derby in 1780, its title decided on the toss of a coin between Lord Derby and Sir Charles Bunbury.

Ewell was the location of Henry VIII's great architectural extravaganza of Nonsuch Palace. This decayed from the 17th century onwards and its site is now a public park. The town is at the source of the Hogsmill River, on the spring line at the edge of the chalk. The river, which enters the Thames at Kingston, provided power for gunpowder mills set up by the Evelyn family at Tolworth, probably in 1561. There were also powder mills at Ewell from the mid 18th to the late 19th century and in the 18th century paper making was carried on alongside corn milling at Ewell Lower Mill.

Among those attracted to the district in the 19th century were artists of the Pre-Raphaelite movement. A powder mill building at Ewell provided the model for the door in Holman Hunt's *Light of the World* and the mill stream was the setting for Millais' painting of the death of Ophelia.

A major source of employment in Epsom has been provided by the five large hospitals for the mentally ill and handicapped which were built by London County Council between 1899 and 1924 on the Horton Estate. These had their own borehole, water pumping station and electricity generator and coal was transported by a railway line, now dismantled, from Ewell West station.

The 20th century has seen the growth of extensive residential areas interspersed with light industry which merge imperceptibly with those of suburban south-west London. Much of historical interest has been lost.

### EE01 OLD WELL HEAD, EPSOM

TQ 192 601 **LSII**　　　　　　　　　　✱

The medicinal spring on Epsom Common was discovered by 1629. In 1690 the Lord of the Manor took an area about 400m in diameter around the well for the development of the spa. This is now occupied by the residential Wells Estate, built since 1950. The old well house was demolished in 1804. A new well-head was erected in 1989. The water was declared unfit for human consumption in 1951 but was found safe in 1986. Stew ponds (✳) to the north [TQ 183 609] were lined with local clay and fed by springs. There are old gravel pits east of the Wells Estate [TQ 196 602].

The New Wells were probably near South Street [TQ 205 606]. Buildings associated with the spa include the 1690 Assembly Rooms, now Waterloo House, in the High Street [TQ 206 607], which is divided into shops.

## EE02 COAL TAX POSTS, EPSOM

TQ 193 597                                                ✳

Stone obelisk by the side of the railway. There is a cast iron post on the A24 road nearby at TQ 194 594.

## EE03 WOODCOTE PARK

TQ 201 589 **LSII**★

Now the RAC Club for members only. A dovecote and barn (**LSII**) of c1770 are visible from Old Barn Road. The grounds also contain two 17th century brick chimneys from a bakehouse or brewhouse and an 18th century well house.

## EE 04 INDOOR RIDING SCHOOL, DURDANS, CHALK LANE

TQ208 595 **LSII**★, **CA**                        ■

At a private house, built 1764-8. A possibly unique riding school with unobstructed 49m x 15m covered floor area, built by Lord Rosebery in 1881. Restoration is in progress.

## EE05 EPSOM GRANDSTAND

TQ 215 585                                              ❏

The Grandstand strictly is the 1927 building which replaced the 1830 stands. To the west are the Club Stands (1927), and to the east the Great War building (1914) and Rosebery Stand (1960). The Prince's Stand (rebuilt 1879) is a separate building (**LSII**) between the Grandstands and the historic Rubbing House public house [TQ 214 585], named after the activity at the end of the race. Major refurbishment is planned in 1990.

Railway stations serving the racecourse were opened at Epsom Downs (LBSCR 1865, replaced 1980s) and Tattenham Corner (SER, 1901).

## EE06 EWELL WEST STATION

TQ 215 627 **LSII**                                  ❏

Original brick-built, 2-storey station with integral station master's house on the LSWR line, opened 1859. Decorative iron brackets to platform canopy.

## EE07 BOURNE HALL MUSEUM, EWELL

TQ 219 627 **CA**                                    ❏

In Bourne Park. A 2m diameter, sheet-iron undershot waterwheel (**LSII**) in the NW corner of the grounds, now a decorative feature, originally drove a pump for the water supply of the former house. A milestone (**LSII**) near the park entrance reads '4 miles to London' (originally 14).

**13**

EE09 Upper Mill, Ewell in 1929                    *Reproduced by courtesy of Bourne Hall Museum*

## EE08 MATHEMATICAL TILES, EWELL

TQ 221 627 **LSII** (*several properties*)   ✳

Good examples can be seen in Church Street of houses faced with mathematical tiles, which have the superficial appearance of bricks.

## EE09 UPPER MILL, KINGSTON ROAD, EWELL

TQ 218 629 **CA** Delisted   ✳

A large three-bay brick and timber corn mill with two-storey luccam, largely reconstructed when converted to offices c1983. The weatherboarded front dated from c1750 and the rest had been rebuilt c1820.

## EE10 LOWER MILL SITE, KINGSTON ROAD, EWELL

TQ 218 631 **CA**

Site of former corn and paper mills. Redeveloped for offices but the mill house (1670, restored 1730s; **LSII**) remains. The old Kingston road (London to Horsham turnpike) was by-passed in 1931-2. There is a smithy (**LSII**) at rear of number 66, and the Eight Bells public house incorporates a toll house.

## EE11 GUNPOWDER SITE, EWELL

TQ 205 642—216 632   ❑

Active c1754-1875. The site has been landscaped as the Hogsmill Open Space. There is an 18th century packhorse bridge [TQ 210 636; **LSII**]. Part of an edge runner stone is visible, another is in a garden path in Church Street, some were reused at Beddington snuff mill and some are buried. The mill owners' house, now Ewell Court, houses a public library.

EE08 Mathematical tiles          *Drawing: P Watkins*

## EE12 TOLWORTH GUNPOWDER SITE

TQ 21 66

Powder mills (c.1561—early 17th century and early 18th century—1854) followed by a corn mill. The river site was cleared c1950 but later remains may survive east of Old Malden Lane.

Gu01 Guildford Mill, c1881          *Reproduced by courtesy of Guildford Museum*

Guildford developed as a market town in the Wey gap through the North Downs. It was a township by the 10th century and its castle is of Norman foundation. The cathedral was consecrated in 1961 and the University moved to the town from Battersea in 1968.

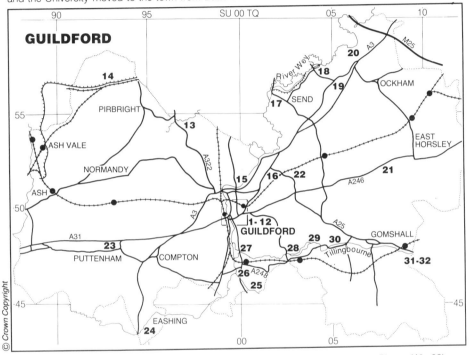

The Wey Navigation, built at the instigation of Sir Richard Weston of Sutton Place (Wk 09) was opened to Guildford in 1653. The chief cargoes to be carried were timber, coal, corn and iron. The Navigation is notable for its early use of pound locks and for the survival of one of its wharfside cranes, the treadwheel crane at Guildford. An extension, the Godalming Navigation, was opened in 1763. Regular barge traffic ceased in 1950 above Guildford and in 1958 to the town itself.

Guildford was a major staging post for road traffic between London and Portsmouth. The town expanded rapidly from the mid 19th century onwards as the centre of a rail network, with links to London in 1845, Reading. Farnham and Redhill in 1849, Portsmouth in 1859 and Horsham in 1865. A new London line completed in 1885, led to extensive suburban development.

Sheep raised on the North Downs provided the basis for a woollen industry which had a high reputation by the 14th century, in particular for 'Guildford blue' cloth dyed with woad. The industry declined in the 17th century as various 'new draperies' grew in popularity.

The Wey and its tributaries, in particular the Tillingbourne, provided power for corn and fulling mills and for other industries from the late 16th century onwards, including gunpowder, metal working and paper making.

Extractive industries have included chalk extraction within and outside the town and sand and gravel working at Send.

**15**

Light engineering developed from the late 19th century onwards, including Drummonds' lathes and Dennis's specialist vehicles. Brewing ceased in 1969 when the Friary Meux brewery closed. A vulcanised fibre works at Shalford and a modern tannery at Gomshall closed in the 1980s but Vokes' engineers, originally filter manufacturers, continue at Normandy.

The town centre has been redeveloped since the early 1960s for offices and shops and a research park associated with the University was established on the outskirts in the 1980s.

### Gu01 TOWN MILL, GUILDFORD

SU 996 492 **LSII**      ✳

A complex of mills existed in this area, with corn mills from at least early medieval times to 1894 and fulling mills by 1251. The 3-storey brick corn mill building in Millbrook, a road created in the early 1960s, dates from 1776 and was extended in 1852. It also housed pumps for the town's water supply, the original pumping system having been set up in the fulling mill in 1701. The 1896 date plaque was affixed when the borough council bought the waterworks and installed new equipment.

In 1966 the water board leased the mill to the adjacent Yvonne Arnaud Theatre for use as workshops. The theatre was built (1965) on the site of the Guildford Foundry of Williams & Filmer, later Filmer & Mason and others.

Behind the theatre in Millmead is the first lock on the Godalming Navigation [**SU** 996 492; **NT**, ❑]. A serious flood occurred in 1968 and sluice gates now allow controlled ˙flooding of former water meadows upstream. Some 200m downstream is the Town Bridge. An iron bridge replaced a medieval stone bridge in 1900, and was rebuilt in 1985 using original components.

### Gu02 TREADWHEEL CRANE, GUILDFORD    *See Illustration: front cover*

SU 994 494 **SC**, **LSII★**, **NT**      ✳

Wey Navigation crane, probably late 17th century, with chain and hook on moveable jib. The treadwheel, 18ft (5.5m) in diameter, is housed in a timber and tiled building. The crane was used until 1908. It was renovated by Guildford Borough Council for the National Trust in 1971 and re-erected on the redeveloped riverside, near its original position on the former Guildford Wharf. The only other comparable crane known to survive in England is at Harwich.

### Gu03 ELECTRICITY WORKS, GUILDFORD

SU 994 495      ✳

Shell of purpose-built public generating station of 1913. The Guildford Electric Supply Company was formed in 1896.

### Gu04 RODBOROUGH BUILDINGS, GUILDFORD

SU 994 495

Probably the oldest surviving purpose-built multi-storey car factory in Britain, erected in 1901 for Dennis Brothers, originally cycle makers. Additional workshops were opened at Woodbridge Hill [**SU** 888 507] in 1905. The Onslow Street building was sold in 1919 to the Rodboro Boot & Shoe Co. Other uses have included engineering and knitwear manufacture. There is a controversial proposal to demolish for road widening.

Dennis Brothers produced private cars until 1913 and then concentrated on specialist vehicles including army tanks, fire engines, commercial vehicles, motor mowers and refuse carts. In 1985 manufacturing ceased at Guildford and the Woodbridge Hill site has been redeveloped as a business park. In 1990 the remaining Dennis Specialist Vehicles Ltd is moving to the Slyfield industrial estate north of the town.

'Dennisville' [**SU** 984 497] is an estate of 102 workers' houses, built in 1933.

### Gu05 WAREHOUSES, WALNUT TREE CLOSE, GUILDFORD

SU 992 497      ✳

Partly erected from 1856 onwards, on an old warehouse site, as Joseph Billings' London Printing Works and let as warehouses when the firm moved to its other premises in 1962. Bishop's Move now occupy the book bindery. Until 1913 this was the bonded warehouse of the Friary Meux brewery, which occupied the site of the present Friary shopping centre.

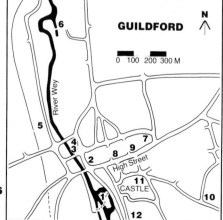

**GUILDFORD**   N ↑

0   100   200   300 M

River Wey

The warehouses have recently been refurbished. Much of the area is now being redeveloped, including Guildford railway station, rebuilt 1988-89

### Gu06 DAPDUNE WHARF, GUILDFORD
SU 993 503 **LSII, NT**  ❑
The timber wharf and boat-building yard adjacent to the Wey Navigation Office are being restored. Features include the blacksmith's shop, steam chest for shaping timber and a recovered Wey barge, the Reliance, which is being rebuilt.

### Gu07 CLOTH HALL, NORTH STREET, GUILDFORD
SU 998 496 **CA**, *Gateway:* **LSII**  ❑
Brick manufactory built in 1629 by George Abbot, a local clothworker's son who became Archbishop of Canterbury. He subsidised linen weaving in an unsuccessful attempt to revive the town's declining textile industry. The building became a house for paupers in 1656 and school from 1856, when the tower was added. Now a retail store.

### Gu08 ANGEL HOTEL, HIGH STREET, GUILDFORD
SU 997 495 **LSII, CA**  ✳
Established before 1527 and the last of the town's five large coaching inns. It has a much restored medieval undercroft, Jacobean timber framing and a facade of 1820. It is to be refurbished as part of a redevelopment plan.

### Gu09 GUILDHALL AND TOWN CLOCK, GUILDFORD
SU 998 495 **SC, LSI, CA**  ✳
The ornate clock projecting from the Guildhall in the High Street is reputedly by John Aylward of London and is assumed to date from 1683 when the facade of the building was added. Restoration of the Guildhall in 1987 revealed Tudor structures.
Tunsgate, the Tuscan portico opposite was part of the corn exchange (1818).

The road surface of the High Street is constructed of granite sets.

### Gu10 SEMAPHORE STATION, PEWLEY HILL
TQ 002 492 **LSII**  ✳
One of the Admiralty signalling stations erected in 1821-2 between London and Portsmouth. The building was used for private accommodation from 1848 and the cupola was added in 1851. Pewley Fort opposite [TQ 003 492; ✳] is one of the mobilisation centres built on the North Downs in the 1890s. Unlike others it has major defensive features. Another example, Henley Fort [SU 982 488; **SC** ✳] is a school camp.

### Gu11 GAS LAMP STANDARD, CASTLE GROUNDS
SU 998 494 **CA**  ✳
Fluted stone Doric pillar with a crevice for gas pipe, c1830, originally at the east end of the Upper High Street.

### Gu12 RACKS CLOSE, GUILDFORD
SU 999 491 **CA**  ❑
From Castle Arch [SU 997 492] a path runs through public gardens to steps leading to an old quarrying area named after the racks or tenter frames on which cloth was stretched to dry. Near the foot of the steps are blocked entrances to 'the Caverns' in which from early medieval times a hard chalk known as clunch was mined for building stone. Chalk was also dug for lime burning at many pits in and near the town and was carried on the Navigation.

### Gu13 RICKFORD MILL, WORPLESDON
SU 965 546 **LSII** ✳
Late 18th century brick corn mill on the Stanford Brook active until 1959. It was converted to a house in 1966, retaining spur wheel and upright shaft, sickle-dressed millstones and gearing associated with an Armfield water turbine of 1906.

### Gu 14 DEEPCUT LOCKS, BASINGSTOKE CANAL
SU 944 569—SU 912 565 **CA**  ❑
*For map of canal, see Woking.*
Flight of 14 locks, numbers 15 to 28, which raise the canal by 29m (95 ft).
Above lock 15 are the brick piers of a viaduct, demolished 1980, of the former Bisley railway branch line (Wk 07).
By Curzon Bridge [SU 920 564] is a high wall built to shield barge horses from the Woking to Southampton railway. A disused army swimming pool near lock 28 was adapted as a workshop when the locks were restored 1977-1983.

**17**

Gu14 Lock 25 and Curzon Bridge, Basingstoke Canal                    *Drawing: R Oliver*

Gu27 Shalford Mill

*Photo: C Shepheard*

### Gu15 STOKE MILL, GUILDFORD

SU 998 510  ✳

Domesday mill site on the River Wey where the first paper mill in Surrey was built c1635 by Sir Richard Weston of Sutton Place (Wk 09). The present 5-storey corn mill of 1879 was built with a waterwheel and stones but became a roller mill powered by water turbines. The adjoining single-storey building (1863) was erected as a half-stuff mill for Eashing paper mill (Gu 33) but became a store for the corn mill in 1869. The corn mill closed in 1957, was later used by a paint and chemicals firm and was converted into offices in 1989.

### Gu16 EDWARD VIII PILLAR BOX, BURPHAM

TQ 016 520  ✳

One of 161 erected in the country.

### Gu17 WEY NAVIGATION WORKSHOP, SEND

TQ 016 557 **NT**  ✳

An old timber-framed workshop containing original tools and equipment, being restored in 1990. Worsfold flood gates adjacent were replaced in 1969 but peg-and-hole paddles were retained.

### Gu18 NEWARK MILL SITE AND EEL TRAP, PYRFORD

TQ 040 575  ✳

Water channels include the River Wey, mill stream, Wey Navigation, flood relief channel of 1935 and a channel for an eel trap, a long iron and brick cage bearing the date 1818 with holes leading to a collecting pit. An exceptionally fine corn mill burned down in 1966. The ruins of the 12th century Newark Abbey (Augustinian) stand nearby.

### Gu19 RIPLEY VILLAGE

TQ 05 56 **CA**

Associated with pioneer cycling. St Mary's Church ❑ has memorials to Herbert Liddell Cortis (d.1885), the first to cycle 20 miles in an hour, and to Harriet and Annie Dibble, landladies of the Anchor hotel. The Hautboy hotel, Ockham [TQ 075 567; ❑] was involved in 1898 in litigation over women's rational dress.

### Gu20 OCKHAM MILL

TQ 056 580 **LSII**  ✳

Four-storey mill of 1862 with terracotta tiles and incised decoration typical of properties owned by the Earl of Lovelace of Horsley Towers [TQ 096 527]. Now a private house but restoration of machinery is in progress.

### Gu21 PUMPING STATION, WEST HORSLEY

TQ 079 523  ✳

On the A246 road, a small 19th century pumping station of the Woking Water & Gas Co, with engine house and chimney stack. Brick-built with cast iron rounded windows. A drinking trough adjacent was erected by the Metropolitan Drinking Fountain & Cattle Trough Association, 1909.

The A246 Guildford to Leatherhead road, turnpiked 1758, by-passes the spring-line villages. It has an almost complete series of Portland stone milestones. There are several disused chalk pits near the road.

There is a fine ice house at Hatchlands, East Clandon [TQ 068 519; **LSI, NT** ❑].

## Gu22 MODEL COTTAGES, MERROW COMMON

TQ 025 518 　　　　　　　　　　　*

Timber cottages for agricultural workers designed by Clough Williams Ellis, which won a competition run by the *Spectator* magazine in 1913. He also designed White Cottage at Newlands Corner [TQ 044 493] which is built of rammed earth. Brick cladding was added in the 1980s.

## Gu23 HOPKILNS, PUTTENHAM

SU 932 478 **CA** 　　　　　　　　　*

A striking but controversial house conversion.

## Gu24 EASHING BRIDGES

SU 946 438 **SC, LSI, CA, NT** 　　　　*

Two medieval stone bridges over the Wey, joined by a causeway.

Eashing mill site **CA**, now redeveloped, was used for paper making 1658-1889. Pewtress Cottages [SU 946 436; **CA**] were built for papermill workers in the 19th century.

## Gu25 GOSDEN COMMON BRIDGES, BRAMLEY

　　　　　　　　　　　　　　　*

TQ 006  457

A roving bridge over the Wey & Arun Canal is incorporated into a later bridge over the canal and the former Horsham to Guildford railway line (1865-1965) which is now followed by the Downs Link footpath.

There was formerly a tanyard adjacent.

A low four-arch aqueduct [TQ 006 456] carries the canal over the Bramley brook. The bridge and aqueduct have been restored by the Wey & Arun Canal Trust and others.

## Gu26 STONEBRIDGE WHARF, GODALMING NAVIGATION

SU 998 466 **NT** 　　　　　　　　❑

A hut on steddle stones was used to store gunpowder awaiting shipment to the Chilworth company's magazines on the Thames at Barking. The modern industrial buildings adja-

cent (1986) replaced a vulcanised fibre factory. The Wey & Arun Junction Canal (1816-71) joins the Navigation at SU 997 464.

## Gu27 SHALFORD MILL

TQ 001 476 **LSII, CA, NT** 　　　　❑

On the Tillingbourne, an early 18th century timber framed, tile-hung corn mill with machinery intact and 3.7m (12ft) diameter low breastshot water wheel. Milling ceased in 1914. The mill was restored and given to the National Trust in 1932 by an anonymous group calling themselves 'Ferguson's Gang'. The storage area was converted into a house.

## Gu28 CHILWORTH GUNPOWDER MILLS

TQ 023 473—TQ 040 480 *Part:* **SC** 　*❑

Established by the East India Company in 1626 and in operation until 1920. The mills were extensive in the late 17th century but then contracted. They expanded in the 19th century, particularly after the introduction of new technology from 1885 onwards.

Materials processing and service buildings west of Blacksmith Lane * have been reused. Paper mills replaced the powder mills at this end of the site [TQ 024 476] in 1704. These were followed by Unwins' printing works from 1871 to 1895 when the factory burned down and the firm moved to Old Woking (Wk 10).

The complex mill ponds and leats are of interest in the middle section of the works **SC** ❑ in which there are numerous edge runner stones and ruins of steam-powered incorporating mills of the 1860s and 1880s. Remains of the 1890s cordite works are on private land on the north bank of the Tillingbourne but some features can be viewed from a public footpath south of the river. This runs east from **TQ 032 477** through the site of the First World War Admiralty cordite works of which few traces remain.

Gu28 Cordite kneading and press house, Chilworth 　　　　*Drawing: R Oliver*

### Gu29 BOTTINGS' MILL, MILL LANE, ALBURY

TQ 039 480                     ✳

At Postford Pond, where a large number of stamp mills were set up in the late 17th century to supply government contracts for gunpowder. These were in decay through the 18th century. Paper mills operated from 1809 to c1870, followed by a flock mill and by corn and animal feed mills.

The roller corn mill of 1910, with original machinery, is due to close in 1990. Animal feed products include fish food for the adjacent trout farm ❑.

A small cast iron water wheel at the trout farm, by Filmer & Mason of Guildford, is from an ornamental lake at Clandon Park and is displayed by permission of the Earl of Onslow.

### Gu30 PIGEON HOUSE, WESTON YARD, ALBURY

TQ 053 478 **CA**                 ✳

In the Albury Estate Office yard, an octagonal brick dovecote of c1550, complete with interior potence for reaching nesting holes. Restored by the Albury Trust.

There is an underground ice-house in the private garden of the adjacent Weston House.

### Gu31 GOMSHALL TANNERY

TQ 084 479                     ✳

Tanning was an important industry of long-standing in the Guildford and Godalming areas. The last Godalming tannery closed in the 1950s but Gomshall tannery was modernised after the Second World War. It closed in 1988 and the future of the site is uncertain. There are 19th century and earlier timber framed buildings including a former bark store and there is a 16th century packhorse bridge.

### Gu32 GOMSHALL MILL

TQ 086 478 **LSII**               ❑

Timber-framed building, at least early 17th century with later extensions, probably on a Domesday mill site. Converted into a restaurant in the 1950s. An interior 18 ft (5.5m) diameter overshot waterwheel has been retained.

# MOLE VALLEY

Dorking, the largest town in the district, is situated at the south end of the Mole gap through the North Downs, in the east-west valley which is known from here eastwards as the Vale of Holmesdale. It developed as a coaching stage and agricultural market town known for a distinctive large breed of poultry, the Dorking Cock, which is still bred. The London to Horsham railway line (1867) and the east-west Reading to Tonbridge line (1849) cross at Dorking and the town still has three railway stations. Dorking is now associated with service industries, in particular insurance and travel companies.

The small town of Leatherhead formerly gained much of its trade from its position at the north end of the Mole gap and on the turnpike road (1758) from Epsom to Guildford. It has notable road and railway bridges, a water pumping and treatment plant on the chalk at the south end of the town and a concentration of modern research establishments.

The spring-line villages between Leatherhead and Guildford became commuter suburbs with the opening of suburban railway lines in 1885. Further south the picturesque scenery of the country around Dorking attracted many wealthy and interesting residents, including a number of French emigres at the time of the French revolution. The area also became popular with day trippers from London with the development of transport. Earlier however it was a flourishing centre of water-powered industry. The Evelyn family, who had gunpowder mills at Tolworth and later Godstone, bought the Wotton estate in the upper Tillingbourne valley in 1579 and established gunpowder, brass and wire mills. Later members of the family, who included John Evelyn, the diarist and author of *Sylva* (1664), carried out notable landscape gardening works. There is a

Wealden iron forge site on the Tillingbourne at Abinger Hammer and in the south there is a furnace and forge site at Ewood [TQ 201 447] and a forge at Leigh [TQ 222 461].

Extractive industries include limeworks on the escarpment of the North Downs and hearthstone mines in the Upper Greensand. There are current sandpits in the Lower Greensand at Buckland and three active brickworks on the Weald clay in the south.

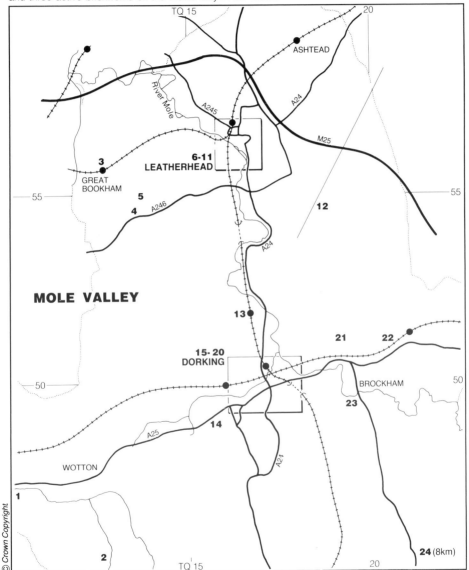

© Crown Copyright

**MV01 THE TILLINGBOURNE, ABINGER**
There are several mill sites on the upper Tillingbourne associated with the Evelyn family and others.

Abinger Hammer [TQ 097 474: **CA** ✳]: An iron forge is recorded from the mid 16th century to c1788. The site has been redeveloped but the masonry of the Old Forge Hole is visible in the bank. The pond has been used for **watercress beds** ✳ since c1850. Traces of leats for water meadows are detectable in fields upstream.

Paddington Mill [TQ 101 471 ✳]: A 19th century brick cornmill with iron pentrough (1867) and remnants of an iron overshot wheel, is on the site of early corn and fulling mills.

Abinger (Crane's) Mill [TQ 110 471]: Used for gunpowder (1589- c1620), copper (17th century) and corn (17th to late 19th century). Remains of a wheel pit survive in the private garden of the mill house (**LSII**).

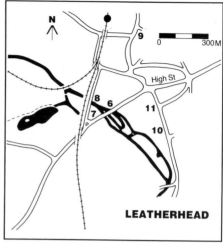

LEATHERHEAD

## MV02 THE TILLINGBOURNE, FRIDAY STREET

TQ 128 458 **CA** ✳

Picturesque mill pond served a cornmill (late 16th century to c1736) and possibly an earlier gunpowder mill. Only a cottage remains below the dam.

Traces of 17th century wire mills and gunpowder mills have been identified near Wotton House [TQ 122 470]. Above the house are ponds and watercourses associated with landscape gardening by the Evelyns.

## MV03 BOOKHAM RAILWAY STATION

TQ 127 556 ❑

Brick and tiled station with cast iron, timber and corrugated sheet canopies, integral station master's house and cast and wrought iron footbridge, built in 1885 for the LSWR Company. Tunnels to east and west are brick with stone dressings and elliptical arch portals.

## MV04 STEAM MILL, GREAT BOOKHAM

TQ 133 549 ✳

A slated brick and stone 3-storey corn mill in Church Road with cast iron window frames, adjoining engine chimney and miller's house has been converted to residential use.

## MV05 DAIRY, GREAT BOOKHAM

TQ 140 550 ✳

On the corner of Eastwick and Lower Roads, a dairy building of c1810, comprising two octagonal brick blocks connected by a passage, with decorative tiling to the roof.

## MV06 LEATHERHEAD TOWN BRIDGE

TQ 163 563 **LSII** ✳

On the River Mole, a brick bridge of 14 arches on medieval stone piers built in 1783 by George Gwilt. There was a ford alongside and a tannery on the upstream side until the 1870s.

## MV07 PUMPING STATION, LEATHERHEAD

TQ 162 563 ✳

Pumping station on the site of the original Leatherhead Water Company works of 1883, of which a yellow brick engine house and chimney survive. The company amalgamated with the East Surrey Water Co in 1927. The present concrete-built pumping station (1936-40) contains 15 Allen S47 diesel pumps. The current boreholes were drilled in 1924, and others were sunk south of the town in 1976 and 1981. The Fetcham springs, in the pond [TQ 159 563] of a

MV04 Leatherhead Bridge

*Photo: C Shepheard*

former cornmill, have been used since 1958. The **Elmer Treatment Works** [TQ 160 556] was originally set up in 1935 as Clark's Works, for water softening by Dr Thomas Clark's quicklime process.

## MV08 LEATHERHEAD RAILWAY BRIDGES

TQ 162 564 ✳

Two fine brick bridges with stone dressings carrying the Dorking line (1863) and the Effingham Junction line (1885) over the River Mole. Best seen from Waterway Road. This was built to give access to the **railway station** [TQ 163 568: ❑], a largely unaltered station of 1867 with polychrome brick, carved stone details and decorative ironwork.

## MV09 SEWAGE GAS VENT PIPE, LEATHERHEAD

TQ 164 567 ✳

Opposite the end of Randalls Road, one of several cast iron vent pipes with spiral embossed decoration near the base and volute finials.

## MV10 CORN CHANDLERY, LEATHERHEAD

TQ 166 562 **CA** ✳

Hutchinson's coal and corn merchants shop, 74 Church Street, partly rebuilt in 1870 but a malt cellar and original stableyard survive.

## MV11 LEATHERHEAD HERITAGE CENTRE

TQ 167 562 **CA** ❑

A small museum at 64 Church Street contains a gravity delivery petrol pump c1930 capable of delivering five brands, an early telephone switchboard, and cast iron direction plates from the nearby crossroads.

## MV12 STANE STREET

TQ 20 58—TQ 18 54 **SC** ✳

East of Ashtead and Leatherhead the line of the Roman road from London to Chichester is followed by lanes and footpaths.

## MV13 BOXHILL & WESTHUMBLE STATION

TQ 167 518 ❑

Built in 1867 on the LBSCR Leatherhead to Horsham line, in polychrome brick with stone dressings. Part of the agreement with the landowner Thomas Grissell was that the station should be 'of an ornamental character'.

## MV14 SONDES PLACE FARM, DORKING

TQ 158 492 ✳

A 19th century model farm in brick and flint, with arched gatehouse featuring a bell cupola and weathervane, converted for sheltered housing since 1986. The land was last worked by tenant farmers in 1921.

## MV15 STATION ROAD, DORKING

TQ 16 49 ✳

**Washway Bridge** [TQ 162 496] over the Pipp Brook, a tributary of the Mole, has a skew construction, seen in the underside brickwork on the west side.

**Parsonage Mill** ✳, on an early watermill site, has been occupied since 1839 by J & W Attlee Ltd (founded 1788), who manufacture animal feed and trade in grain and agricultural supplies. The present mill was built in 1951.

A modern business park is on the site of the former gas works. The houses in **Portland Road** opposite have large capital letters set in the brickwork instead of numbers.

MV13 Boxhill and Westhumble Station
*Drawing: R Oliver*

## MV16 DORKING MUSEUM

TQ 164 494 **CA** ❑

Housed in the former foundry (1825) in West Street which closed c1960.

## MV17 STREET FURNITURE, DORKING

TQ 16 49 **CA** *Some:* **LSII** ✳

Dorking town centre is exceptionally well endowed with cast iron bollards, handrails and lamp standards, including a pump and guide-

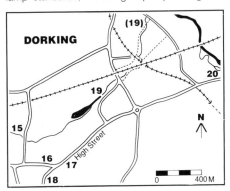

MV17 Street furniture, Dorking    *Photo: C Shepheard*

post at the junction of High Street and South Street. Mainly erected 1882-91 by Dorking District Local Board and 1901-13 by Dorking Urban District Council.

## MV18 DORKING SAND CAVES
TQ 164 493 **CA**    *By arrangement:* ☐
Workings in the Lower Greensand entered in South Street are interpreted as a gentleman's folly. They were used as wine cellars until the 1960s.

## MV19 PIPPBROOK MILL, DORKING
TQ 170 500 **LSII**    ✳
Closed as a corn mill 1933 and rebuilt as offices after a fire in 1979. The overflow weir is a long slot in the middle of the mill stream which takes the water under the building. There are external and internal wheel pits.
Pixham Mill [TQ 174 506 **LSII** ✳], now a dwelling house, can be reached by footpaths leading under railway bridges from the east side of the A24.

## MV20 CASTLE MILL, DORKING
TQ 180 502 **LSII**    ✳
On the River Mole. Made animal feed up to the 1950s, sold in 1969 and converted into a private house. Much of the external breast-shot wheel survives.

**24**

## MV21 BROCKHAM CHALK PITS AND LIMEWORKS
TQ 19 51 *Kilns:* **LSII**    ✳
The chalkpits and limeworks were taken over in 1881 by the Brockham Brick Co, which owned adjacent brick fields on the Gault clay and hearthstone mines below the chalk. The manager Alfred Bishop patented his continuous 'Brockham' lime kiln in 1889. One substantially complete example and remains of several others survive on the site. The Brockham Lime & Hearthstone Co Limited (1911) later became a subsidiary of the Dorking Greystone Lime Co Ltd at Betchworth (MV 22). Brickmaking ceased c1909, hearthstone mining in 1925 and lime-burning in 1934.
The works had a standard gauge railway siding from the SER Reading-Tonbridge line (1849). A museum of narrow gauge stock from Betchworth and elsewhere, set up in 1962, was hampered by poor access over a level crossing [TQ 198 507]. This has a brick crossing keeper's cottage and SER/LSWR cast iron notices. In 1979 the museum amalgamated with the newly formed Amberley Chalk Pits Museum in Sussex.

## MV22 BETCHWORTH CHALK PITS AND LIMEWORKS
*See photo on back cover*
TQ 20 51 *Kilns:* **LSII**    ✳
Worked 1865-1934 by the Dorking Greystone Lime Company and closed in 1960. There are two rows of lime kilns with brick built charging towers (1867) plus important examples of later Dietzch kilns, double kilns with split flues. To reach the grey Lower Chalk, quantities of Middle Chalk were stripped and dumped, as also at Brockham.
A programme of infilling, land reclamation and conservation of industrial features has begun. The North Downs Way footpath crosses the site.

## MV23 BOROUGH BRIDGE, BROCKHAM
TQ 196 497 **CA**    ✳
Narrow brick bridge over the Mole dated 1737, with large flood relief tunnel in the buttress.

## MV24 LOWFIELD HEATH WINDMILL, CHARLWOOD
TQ 235 408 **LSII**    ✳
A tall post mill formerly at **TQ 270 399**, which was originally in Surrey but in Sussex since 1974. It was built c1760, was last worked by wind in 1880. It became derelict but could not be restored on its original site near Gatwick Airport. It was dismantled by the Lowfield Heath Windmill Trust in 1987 and is being rebuilt at Gatwick Aviaries and Zoo.

The North Downs are crossed by the Merstham gap, the route used by the historic Croydon, Merstham & Godstone Railway which opened in 1805. This early plateway continued the Surrey Iron Railway, which followed the Wandle valley, to quarries and chalk pits at Merstham. The line was bought out in 1838 by the London & Brighton Railway Company which had settled for the direct route to Brighton via Merstham. Redhill developed at the junction of the Brighton line (1841) and the SER line to Ashford (1842) and Reading (1849). Transport structures include traces of the CM&GR, tunnels on the 1841 railway line to Brighton and the parallel 'Quarry line' (1899) which by-passes Merstham and Redhill, and the Redhill tunnel on the Quarry line.

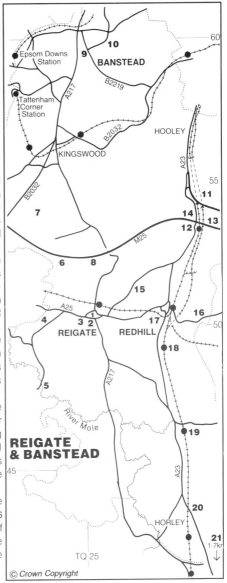

Other features include water towers on the Downs, windmills and remains of various industries, among which the extractive industries predominate.

There were large chalk pits at Reigate and Merstham. The Upper Greensand yields both a hard calcareous firestone, used for building until the 19th century, and softer hearthstone which was used for whitening steps and floors. Many old firestone mines were reworked for hearthstone when its use became fashionable in the 19th century. Sand extraction in the Lower Greensand is conspicuous today at the large Holmthorpe sand-pits, with their standard gauge railway to the main line north of Redhill. In Reigate, silver sand workings go back at least to the medieval period. Haphazard tunnelling west of the town centre caused cottages to collapse in the mid 19th century and in the 1980s some of the ground has been stabilised by infilling with waste from fuller's earth pits.

Fuller's earth, from the Sandgate Beds of the Lower Greensand, was extracted for centuries for the woollen industry. Modern uses include sealing and lubrication products, carriers for agricultural chemicals and foundry bonding clays, but 40% is now sold as cat litter. Available deposits in the area are nearly worked out.

Brickmaking has long been important on the Weald clay, for instance at Earlswood [TQ 286 476 and TQ 270 483]. A knot sculpture made of handmade bricks from Redland's active Beare Green works, south of Dorking, stands outside Redland House in Reigate [TQ 255 503].

**25**

The main A23 road closely follows the London to Brighton railway line. Modern development is almost continuous along this route, from the outskirts of Greater London to the vicinity of Gatwick international airport.

## RB01 REIGATE ROAD TUNNEL AND SAND MINES

TQ 253 504 **CA** ✳

Tunnel, now pedestrian, constructed in 1823 through the castle mound to eliminate a sharp bend in the Crawley to Sutton road. Sand workings on both sides, some of which evidently pre-date the road tunnel, have been used for ammunition storage in the First World War, air-raid shelters in the Second, and for wine storage. One is now used by a small-bore rifle club.

Medieval (?) sand workings in the castle mound are to be opened to the public in 1990 at limited times.

## RB02 REIGATE PRIORY GATES

TQ 253 500 **CA** ✳

Fine wrought iron gates made from Sussex iron in 1710 can be seen from the park to the west. The house (**SC, LSII**), last rebuilt in 1776, is now a school.

## RB03 BELLINGHAM'S SHOP, REIGATE

TQ 250 502 **LSII, CA** ❑

Victorian butcher's shop front, porticoed and marbled, at 77 High Street.

## RB04 REIGATE HEATH WINDMILL

TQ 234 501 **LSII**★ ❑

A mid 18th century post mill last operated c1868. In 1880 the roundhouse was converted into a chapel of ease to St Mary's Parish Church, Reigate and monthly services are held in summer. Restored by the local Council in 1964 with only decorative sweeps but most of the internal machinery intact.

Traces of **Reigate Heath racecourse** can be seen west of Flanchford Road [**TQ 238 503**]. This was active 1834-9, for meetings following Epsom Races.

## RB05 FLANCHFORD MILL

TQ 235 479 **LSII** ✳

On the Wallace Brook near its confluence with the River Mole, near a public footpath. Privately owned small 3-storey two pair corn mill with decayed external wooden breastshot wheel and machinery intact. A mill was mentioned in 1527 but the present brick and weatherboarded building dates from 1768.

## RB06 CARRUTHERS', PITT'S AND COLLEY HILL MINES

**26** TQ 245 519

Hearthstone mines opened c1890 were worked by Reigate Mines Ltd until 1961. There was a small factory outside the mine for cutting the stone and processing it for hearthstone powder and moulded blocks. All work ceased 1965 and the buildings have been removed.

There are older firestone workings to the west (Carruthers') and the east (Pitt's). There are public rights of way nearby but there is no access to mine galleries and the area is overgrown.

## RB07 COAL TAX WALK, BANSTEAD HEATH ✳

Ten cast iron City of London coal tax posts (**LSII**) can be seen along a circular route between Dorking Road [**TQ 230 548**], Mogador Road [**TQ 240 530**] and Brighton Road [**TQ 243 548**]. They were restored and repainted by Banstead Commons Conservators.

There are **Victorian letterboxes** (flat type) at Mogador [**TQ 239 528**] and Brighton Road [**TQ 242 554**].

## RB08 NORTH DOWNS WAY, REIGATE

**NT** *Passes several features of interest:*

**Colley Hill water tower** [**TQ 244 523**]. Sutton & District Water Company tower, built 1911.

**Reigate Hill water tower** [**TQ 257 521**]. East Surrey Water Company, built 1925. There is a BBC TV relay station mast adjacent.

**Chalk pit** [**TQ 254 518**]. Used in the Second World War as Montgomery's HQ before D-Day.

**Mobilisation centre**, Reigate Hill [**TQ 257 521 SC**]. One of the 'forts' built along the crest of the North Downs 1890-6.

## RB09 WATER PUMP, GARRATTS LANE, BANSTEAD

TQ 251 593 **LSII** ✳

Cast iron trough with remains of hand pump, possibly 18th century.

## RB10 WELL, PARK ROAD, BANSTEAD

TQ 259 599 **LSII** ✳

Medieval village well with 18th century timber covering.

## RB11 RAILWAY TOWER, MERSTHAM

TQ 290 547 ✳

Brick alignment tower built in 1838 for the construction of the Merstham railway tunnel on the LBSCR/SER line.

## RB12 CROYDON, MERSTHAM & GODSTONE RAILWAY

Traces of the CM&GR are largely hidden by later road and railway developments. The line served the chalk pits of the Merstham Greystone Limeworks [**TQ 29 54**] which were develo-

RB12 Croydon, Merstham & Godstone Railway display at Merstham          *Drawing: R Oliver*

ped in the early 19th century by Jolliffe & Banks, promoters of the railway. The chalk pits were filled with Croydon refuse and later built over by the M23 motorway (1972). The CM&GR terminus, now also under the M23, was at the Quarry Dean firestone mines [TQ 298 539]. Surviving features include:
Display, Quality Street [TQ 289 533: **CA** ☐]. Four CM&GR plate rails and two millstones for lime, in a small public garden.
Weighbridge Cottage [TQ 288 544 **LSII** ✳]. CM&GR weighing house and toll house, built of Merstham firestone. Now a private house.
Railway cutting [TQ 286 554–286 535 **SC**]. On the east side of the A23, running north from opposite Harps Oak Lane to the motorway junction and then continuing as shallow depressions in front gardens.
Dean Lane Bridge, Hooley [TQ 287 558] The parapet and top of the arch of a brick overbridge.
Fox Shaw [TQ 286 539 **LS**]. Formerly the Fox Inn. A plaque commemorates Edward Banks' wager on the weight one horse could pull on the railway.

### RB13 CHALDON AND MERSTHAM STONE QUARRIES
TQ 281 536—323 535
Underground quarries which were the source of much of the 'Reigate stone' used for building in medieval London, as an alternative to Caen stone from Normandy. Mining continued into the 19th century when the CM&GR provided

transport. The workings are drift mines, worked down dip to the water table and then extended along the strike, forming a network of pillars and stalls. Waste material was backfilled behind dry stone walls. This series was not reworked for hearthstone and some of the older galleries are coated with calcite formations. Extensive surveys and photographic records have been made by Subterranea Britannica and other bodies.

### RB14 LYCH GATE, MERSTHAM CHURCH
TQ 291 538                                         ✳
Made from remains of Merstham windmill, dismantled when the loop-line of the London-Brighton railway was built in 1896. The cast iron windshaft forms the central support and two peak millstones are set in the path.
Tombstone near the north end of the church to Henry Hoof, contractor of the London & Brighton railway, who died (in his bed) in 1840.

### RB15 WRAY COMMON WINDMILL
TQ 269 511 **LSII★**, **CA**                      ✳
Tower mill built in 1824. There is no internal machinery and the building has suffered storm damage since it was restored.

### RB16 FULLER'S EARTH WORKS, REDHILL                                    ✳
A path runs from the A25 [TQ 285 510] towards the London to Brighton 'Quarry line' through an area worked at least from the 17th century and **27** now partly reclaimed for housing. The active Nutfield Quarry [TQ 293 511] has been worked

since the early 1970s for fuller's earth at lower levels and sand above. Copyhold Works [TQ 288 502] was modernised by Laporte Industries in 1982. The earth is dried and screened for cat litter and some is calcined to produce granules for carrying agricultural chemicals.

Chart Lodge on the A25 was built in 1780 by John William Grece, a specialist entrepreneur who opened the Chartfield pit [TQ 287 501].

Old underground workings have been found near the processing plant of Patterson Court [TQ 293 503], and near Fuller's Wood Lane. Some terrain shows evidence of workings but there has been much infilling with refuse and land reclamation.

### RB17 BARK BARN, OAKDENE ROAD, REDHILL

TQ 275 503 **LSII**     ✳

Fine late 18th century wooden barn, all that remains of the Redhill tannery. Used as offices.

### RB18 BRITISH WAX REFINING COMPANY, EARLSWOOD

TQ 280 493     ✳

Family firm founded in 1913 which purifies beeswax and other waxes, for use in cosmetics. The original equipment is used.

### RB19 MONOTYPE CORPORATION, SALFORDS

TQ 287 463     ✳

Founded in 1899 to manufacture 'Monotype' compositing machines and now producing machinery for laser and photographic printing. Clay for bricks for the factory was dug on site and the pit forms an ornamental pond. There is an estate of 24 workers' houses built in the early years in Dunraven Avenue.

### RB20 HORLEY BREWERY

TQ 287 433     ✳

Built as the Albert Brewery c1869 and extended in 1890, sold in 1904 to Page and Overton of Croydon and closed down in 1917. Still intact but since used as a laundry and warehouses and now by a firm manufacturing pumps.

### RB21 'THE BEEHIVE', GATWICK AIRPORT

TQ 285 399     ✳

Lost to West Sussex in 1974. The circular control tower and terminal building erected in 1936 is now used as offices. Nearby are platform faces of the original railway station which closed when the present airport was developed farther north. A pedestrian tunnel to the station survives.

RB21 Gatwick Airport in 1936

*Photo: John King Collection*

The modern borough is named after the site associated with the signing of the Magna Carta in 1215. It contains residential areas bordering Windsor Great Park, the lake of Virginia Water created for William, Duke of Cumberland between 1748 and 1757, and the High Victorian Royal Holloway College at Egham and Holloway Sanatorium at Virginia Water, built by the pill manufacturer Thomas Holloway in the 1880s.

The most numerous industrial features are associated with transport. The Thames forms the north-eastern boundary of the borough and the Basingstoke Canal enters the Wey Navigation in the south. City of London coal tax posts on the borough boundary are in general listed under Spelthorne.

The main road route from London to the South West (the modern A30), which has been used since Roman times, was turnpiked in 1728 by the Bedfont & Bagshot Turnpike Trust. A nearly complete set of milestones remains.

A branch from the main LSWR line at Weybridge was built to Chertsey in 1848. The present Chertsey station was built in 1866 when the line was extended to join the Staines to Wokingham line (1856) at Virginia Water.

There are worked-out sand and gravel pits both on higher ground and on the Thames flood plain. Brick and tile making have been carried on for centuries, the most important product being the fine inlaid tiles produced at Chertsey Abbey in the 13th century.

Public service industries have been concentrated near the Thames at Egham. Manufacturing industries have included Lagonda cars and Petter diesel engines at Egham. The proximity of Brooklands brought the early aircraft industry to Addlestone, where the Plessey works is still active.

### Ru01 THE RIVER THAMES, EGHAM ✻

A footpath runs along the right bank of the Thames from the Berkshire boundary to Staines (see also Spelthorne). Following the river downstream, features include:

Nicholes boatyard, Yardmead [TQ 012 722]

Bell Weir Lock [TQ 017 720]. Built in 1817 and named after its first lock keeper; rebuilt in 1867, 1877 and 1973-4.

The Glanty [TQ 021 718]. Remains of berths and wharves.

Egham Hythe [TQ 037 714]. Remains of berths and wharves, crossed by a footbridge, immediately below Staines bridge.

Tims Boatyard [TQ 036 710]. Active yard near Staines railway bridge.

### Ru02 EGHAM CAUSEWAY

TQ 031 715—TQ 006 713 ✻

An embankment 1-2m high and 3-4m wide was built by Thomas de Oxenford, a 13th century wool merchant, to keep his packhorse route free from flooding. The eastern half of the Causeway is followed by the pavement of the A308 road west of Staines Bridge and the western half is under the Egham Bypass. Proximity to coal traffic on the Thames led to the siting of gas and electricity works on the Causeway. The gas works of the Staines & Egham Gas Light and Coke Company [TQ 026 710] ceased production in the 1960s. A large dry gasholder (1928) was demolished in 1985, but a smaller earlier one remains. The Staines & Egham Electricity Company power station (1904) was demolished in 1986 and the site has been used for offices [TQ 027 716].

The North Surrey Water Company waterworks [TQ 022 717], built on the Causeway in the 1880s, has been modernised and expanded several times.

### Ru03 LAGONDA CAR FACTORY, EGHAM

TQ 029 714

Commonly associated with Staines because of its postal address, the works was established by Wilbur Gunn to manufacture motor bicycles and tricycles and later cars, which were named after Gunn's home town in Ohio. After making munitions in the First World War the firm had its heyday in the 1930s producing large sports cars. Petter's diesel engine works which fol- **29** lowed closed in 1989 and is to be demolished.

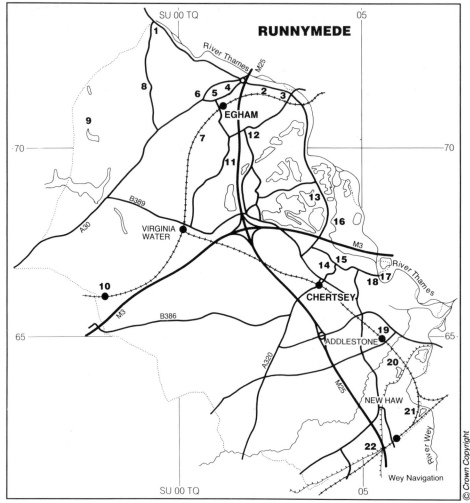

© Crown Copyright

## Ru04 MILESTONE, EGHAM HIGH STREET

TQ 014 715 **LSII**  ✳

Erected in 1743 at 18 miles from London (Hyde Park Corner) and recently relocated in the garden wall of new houses. Further milestones survive at 19-22 miles from London and the series continues in Surrey Heath.

The cast iron hand pump in Walnut Tree Gardens [TQ 008 712] was moved from near Runnymede Bridge when the M25 was built. It was originally used for laying dust on the turnpike road.

## Ru05 MALTHOUSE, EGHAM

TQ 010 714 **LSII**  ✳

19th century building, on north of High Street, restored and converted to offices.

Egham Museum is in the Literary Institute opposite [TQ 010 713 LSII ☐]

## Ru06 TOWER GARAGE, EGHAM

TQ 006 713 **LSII**  ✳

1930s style garage on the Egham bypass.

## Ru07 EGHAM WORKS, RUSHAM ROAD

TQ 005 705  ✳

Established c1930 by Foster Wheeler, an American boiler making firm which left in 1967. It has since become a factory estate accommodating several small businesses.

## Ru08 CATTLE TROUGH, ENGLEFIELD GREEN

SU 992 718 **CA**  ✳

Metropolitan cattle trough facing the north side of the Green.

Tite Hill (B388) and Bishopsgate Road are on

the line of an old road to Reading through Windsor Great Park. **Milestones** remain at 19 and 20 miles from London [SU 998 713 and SU 984 720].

### Ru09 GRAVEL PIT, WINDSOR GREAT PARK ✱
The Heather Garden [SU 971 696] is an example of a disused dry gravel pit on high ground, worked before the First World War to supply gravel for roads in the Park. Cow Pond [SU 975 715] and Obelisk Pond [SU 974 701] are fishponds created by 1607 and in 1750 respectively.

### Ru10 MILITARY VEHICLE ESTABLISHMENT CHOBHAM COMMON
**SU 980 660**
Opened during the Second World War, and now known as Royal Armaments Research & Development Establishment (RARDE). Longcross Station on the Staines to Wokingham branch line was built in 1942 to serve the establishment, which had its own siding, still partly visible.

### Ru11 TITHE BARN, GREAT FOSTERS, EGHAM
**TQ 012 696 LSII** ❏
Moved from Ewell c1930 to become the Great Hall of the 16th century manor house of Great Fosters **LSI**.

### Ru12 OLD PIPE HOUSE, THORPE
**TQ 018 701** ✱
The private house with a clock, on the corner of Clockhouse Lane, was formerly used for making clay pipes.

### Ru13 THORPE PARK
**TQ 039 687** ❏
Extensive gravel workings landscaped into ornamental lakes as a 'theme park' and water sports centre, entered from the A320 road. There is a restored timber-framed, weather-boarded granary on steddle stones within the park at **TQ 025 688**.

### Ru14 CHERTSEY MUSEUM, WINDSOR STREET
**TQ 040 670 LSII, CA** ❏
Examples of work by the local Herring's iron foundry (closed c1982, demolished 1989). Also displays on early aircraft manufacture at Addlestone by Bleriot and the SPAD Company, and by Lang's propellers and their successors, Airscrew and Airscrew-Howden.

### Ru15 HAND PUMP, WINDSOR STREET, CHERTSEY
**TQ 042 669 LSII, CA** ✱
Presented to the town by John Ivatt Briscoe, MP, 1863. Cast by a London foundry.

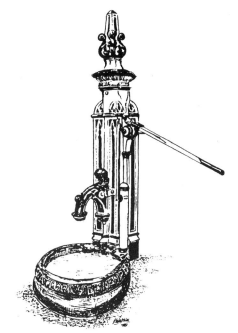

Ru15 Chertsey pump          *Drawing: P Watkins*

### Ru16 THE ABBEY RIVER, CHERTSEY
**TQ 042 689—TQ 053 670** ✱
A 5km long watercourse which was used to power the mills of the Benedictine Chertsey Abbey (founded AD 666), as illustrated on a late 15th century cartulary in the Public Record Office. The Abbey was destroyed after the Dissolution. but three fish ponds **SC** ❏ created by Abbot Rutherwycke in the 14th century survive in public gardens [TQ 042 672].

### Ru17 LOCK KEEPER' COTTAGE, CHERTSEY LOCK
**TQ 054 668 LSII** ✱
Neglected cottage on the east bank of the Thames. The lock was built in 1813 and rebuilt in 1913. There are cast iron coal tax posts at TQ 055 667 and TQ 054 669.

### Ru18 CHERTSEY BRIDGE
**TQ 053 666 SC, LSII** ✱
A 7-arched stone bridge over the Thames built 1780-85 by James Paine, with minor alterations 1894. There is a cast iron coal tax post at the east end. The bridge was featured by Charles Dickens in *Oliver Twist*, when Bill Sykes and Olive went to burgle a house. Bates Boatyard is at TQ 054 664.

### Ru19 PLESSEY WORKS, ADDLESTONE
**TQ 057 650** ✱ **31**
Factory established in 1916 by Louis Bleriot to make war planes. It was bought in 1927 by

Weyman Motor Bodies, who made buses, ambulances and military vehicles and coach-built bodies for cars. Since 1966 the site has been occupied by Plessey, manufacturers of radar equipment etc.

Lang's propeller works site in Ham Moor Lane [TQ 063 648] is now a modern trading estate.

## Ru20 COXE'S LOCK MILL

TQ 061 641 **LSII**         ✳

Established on the Wey Navigation c1777 as an iron mill. It was associated with Alexander Raby and Obadiah Wix Rogers and later with John Bunn. It was a silk mill and corn mill in the 1830s. Corn milling continued until the early 1980s and corn was regularly delivered by barge until 1969, when the grain terminals were moved from London Docks to Tilbury. An attempt to revive this trade was made in the 1970s. The present late 19th century building was converted into apartments in 1989.

## Ru21 RAILWAY BRIDGES, RIVER WEY

TQ 06 63         ✳

Seven Arches Bridge [TQ 068 630] on the London to Southampton main line and Nine Arches Bridge [TQ 065 632] on the Addlestone to Byfleet line can be viewed from a footpath running east from the vicinity of New Haw lock at [TQ 055 630]. The pond was created by excavations for the railway embankments.

## Ru22 BASINGSTOKE CANAL

TQ 055 620—TQ 035 610 **CA**     ✳

The last section to be restored. A footbridge, rebuilt 1988, crosses from the east bank of the Wey Navigation to the south bank of the canal [TQ 055 620]. Five of the six Woodham locks are in Runnymede. Scotland Bridge [TQ 046 616] is an original brick arch canal bridge. There is a lock keeper's cottage at lock 3 [TQ 040 612].

Ru20 Coxe's Lock Mill          *Photo: C Shepheard*

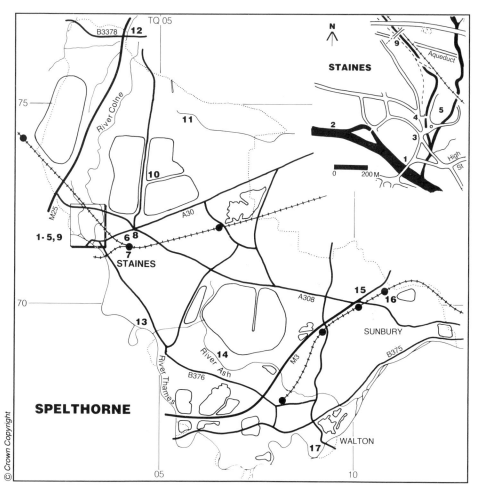

SPELTHORNE

The ancient name of Spelthorne was revived in 1974 for the part of Surrey north of the Thames which historically had belonged to Middlesex.

Staines was the bridging point for the Roman road to Silchester and for, the Bedfont & Bagshot Turnpike road which became the A30.

Features along the Thames (see also Runnymede) include Penton Hook and Shepperton locks, Staines railway bridge and Staines, Chertsey and Walton road bridges. Some thirteen coal tax posts occur at the borough boundary along the Thames and on roads leading west.

The River Colne, which enters the Thames at Staines, feeds two long artificial watercourses, the 16th century Duke of Northumberland's River and the 17th century Longford River. These skirt the boundary of Heathrow Airport in the north of the borough.

Manufacturing industries developed from the mid 19th century onwards, in particular the making of linoleum for which Staines became known around the world. Other industries included brewing,

**33**

mineral water, and the manufacture of candles which ended in a spectacular fire in 1924. Proximity to London brought the entertainment industry, represented by Kempton Park racecourse and Shepperton film studios.

In the 20th century the formerly rural landscape has been transformed by housing development, gravel digging, the building of motorways and the creation of reservoirs for London's water supply.

### Sp01 STAINES BRIDGE
TQ 032 715 **LSII**, **CA** ✳

Bridge of three stone arches over the Thames, built by John and George Rennie in 1829-32. It was widened in 1958.

Two **coal tax posts LSII** stand on the south bank. The **Three Counties Post** nearby [**TQ 027 717**, **LSII**] is at the point where Surrey, Buckinghamshire and Middlesex formerly met. The present Staines bridge is 200m upstream from earlier crossings. Its construction necessitated the building of Bridge Street and Clarence Street with bridges over the River Colne at Clarence Street and Church Street.

### Sp02 THE LONDON STONE, STAINES
TQ 027 717 (*original* **LSII**) ✳

In Ashby Recreation Ground, a replica of the stone erected in 1285 to mark the limit of the City of London's jurisdiction over the Thames. The original is at Staines Library [**TQ 036 713**]. The stone later served as a coal tax post. There is also a cast iron obelisk **coal tax post** in Wraysbury Road [**TQ 026 720**], moved from near Wraysbury railway station.

### Sp03 ASHBY'S BREWERY, STAINES
TQ 032 717 **CA** (*malthouse & tower* **LSII**) ✳

Founded in the 18th century by Thomas Ashby, a Quaker, at 57 Church Street. The malthouse in his back garden survives. The business sold out in 1931 to Simmonds of Reading which became part of Courage's in the 1960s. Brewing ceased in the 1950s and bottling in 1970s. Only a tower of 1903 remains and is being converted into flats. The rest of the site is occupied by Courage's offices and car parks.

### Sp04 STAINES WEST STATION
TQ 033 718 **LSII**, **CA** ✳

Station, closed 1981, on the Staines & West Drayton Railway. The single line, opened in 1885, was intended to join the LSWR system at Staines. However it was taken over by the GWR which insisted on a separate terminus, for which a dwelling house was converted. Closed in 1981, the station building has been restored as offices. Part of the line disappeared under the M25 but at Staines a connection to the Windsor line continues to serve an oil depot.

The house was formerly occupied by the Quaker Finch family who owned an adjacent
34 mustard mill on the Wraysbury River, NE of the house in Mustard Mill Road. Only parts of the mill race have survived.

### Sp05 CENTRAL TRADING ESTATE
TQ 034 718—TQ 037 717 ✳

A calico printing works on this site was bought in 1864 by Frederick Walton, patentee of linoleum and founder of the Linoleum Manufacturing Company. Power was provided by the Colne and Wraysbury rivers. With the development of vinyl floorings the works closed in 1973 and the site became a trading estate. Some of the old buildings remain.

The nearby Renshaw Industrial Estate [**TQ 036 719**] was the site of the Renshaw Foundry whose products included manhole covers, many of which can be seen in the district.

### Sp06 HARRIS'S BREWERY, STAINES
TQ 040 715 ✳

Built in 1824-51, bought up by Ashby's (Sp 03) in 1903 and soon afterwards closed. The oast house, brewer's house and granary have been adapted for community use, but a surviving malthouse is at risk of demolition.

### Sp07 STAINES STATION
TQ 041 714 ❑

On the Windsor, Staines & South Western Railway line from Richmond to Datchet (1848) and Windsor (1851) and the Staines, Wokingham & Woking Railway line to Wokingham (1856). The station was much rebuilt after electrification in 1930 and the goods yard closed in the 1960s.

**Staines railway bridge** [**TQ 036 712**] is a wrought iron girder bridge on the Wokingham line, built 1856. There is a cast iron obelisk **coal tax post** on the approach, on the north side of the line at **TQ 036 713**.

### Sp08 STAINES BUS GARAGE
TQ 042 718 ✳

Built in 1934. Described by Pevsner as a good, early example of the Modern Movement in English architecture.

### Sp09 CATTLE BRIDGE
### AND STAINES MOOR
TQ 031 723 ❑

Composite bridge built for cattle grazing on the common land of Staines Moor: a twin arch yellow brick bridge over the Wraysbury River, a single arch red brick bridge (1848) over the Windsor railway line, and a steel plate girder bridge (1885) over the GWR branch line to Staines West. It gives pedestrian access to the surviving common between the King George VI and Wraysbury reservoirs, a Site of Special

Sp04 Staines West Station      *Photo: C Shepheard*

Scientific Interest (SSSI) under constant threat of gravel extraction. A **herdsman's cottage** near the bridge was erected in 1900 by the Committee of Commoners with funds received for loss of common rights.

### Sp10 STAINES RESERVOIRS
TQ 046 730      ❑
The first in the district, built by the West Middlesex Water Co in .1897-1902. Two reservoirs with a footpath along the dividing bar.

### Sp11 DUKE OF NORTHUMBERLAND'S RIVER AND LONGFORD RIVER
TQ 05 75—08 74      ✳
On the boundary of Heathrow Airport. The Duke of Northumberland's River was dug in the 16th century to supply Syon Abbey's watermill at Twickenham and the Longford River was created in the 17th century to supplement the water supply to ornamental fountains at Hampton Court Palace.

### Sp12 MAD BRIDGE, COLNBROOK
TQ 041 766      ✳
Disused bridge carrying the old Bath Road over the Wraysbury River. The road was diverted when the M25 was built and the 16 milestone from London, Hyde Park Corner was moved to the embankment leading to the new bridge.

### Sp13 PENTON HOOK LOCK
TQ 043 694      ❑
The highest of the City of London locks on the Thames, first opened in 1815. The original lock keeper's cottage, **LSII**, still stands.

### Sp14 SHEPPERTON FILM STUDIOS
TQ 067 686   *Entrance:* **LSII**
Established in 1928 by Norman Lander at Littleton House. The River Ash represented a mighty African river in *Sanders of the River* (1930). Rebuilt by Alexander Korda's British Lion Co in 1946, the heyday of the studios was in the 1950s and 1960s. Now owned by Lee International Film Studio.

### Sp15 FACTORIES, HANWORTH ROAD, SUNBURY
TQ 103 703      ✳
The 19th century **mineral water works** of Cantrell & Cochrane's was taken over by Coca Cola in the 1970s and closed in 1987. Now a depot. Some old buildings survive.

Sp12 Mad Bridge, Colnbrook      *Drawing: P Watkins*

The adjacent **Sundeala Hardboard Factory** which is still active was established by D M Sutherland, inventor of hardboard (wood fibre board) and founder of the Patent Impermeable Millboard Company (PIM) in 1898.

### Sp16 KEMPTON PARK RACECOURSE
TQ 110 700  ❏
Opened in 1878 and still in use. In 1878 a new station for racegoers was opened on the Thames Valley Railway Company's Fulwell to Shepperton line.

### Sp17 WALTON BRIDGE
TQ 092 665  ✳
A temporary Bailey bridge is in use today. The brick approaches survive of the wooden bridge (1750) which was painted by Canaletto and Turner and was replaced ˙ in 1780 by Smeaton. A new iron bridge (1863) was damaged in the Second World War and eventually demolished in 1986. There is an original **toll house** on the Shepperton side and a **coal tax post** on the south bank.

# SURREY HEATH

The heathland on the Bagshot Sands of north-west Surrey was sparsely populated until the 19th century. Until then the main commercial activity was associated with the road from London to the South-West which became the A30. Bagshot, on routes from Winchester to Windsor and London to Exeter, developed as a stage for travellers, particularly at the height of the coaching era in the early 19th century.

The Basingstoke Canal and the London to Southampton railway line in the south of the borough show interesting engineering features.

The heaths provide sites for army camps and training grounds and Camberley owes its origin to military establishments. The town developed from York Town and Cambridge Town which respectively grew up around the Sandhurst Royal Military College in Berkshire which opened in 1812 and the Staff College which was founded after the Crimean War and opened in 1862.

The area was not well served by local railways until the Ascot to Ash Vale line was built in 1878. From then onwards it developed as a residential area made fashionable by the residences of the Duke of Connaught, the Empress Eugenie and the Crown Prince of Siam.

Several mills existed on the Windle Brook, a tributary of the Wey which flows through Bagshot, but little of these survives. The light, sandy soils of the district have been used for nursery gardening since the late 18th century by several nationally known firms including Waterers and Fromows.

Industrial development of the area was largely delayed until the 20th century and more particularly until after the Second World War. Since then large industrial estates have grown up, for example in the York Town and Bridge Road areas of Camberley, and population growth has been rapid. Extensive gravel extraction has been carried out in the Blackwater valley in recent decades and reclamation is now in progress.

### SH 01 THE BASINGSTONE
SU 897 619  ✳
Parish boundary stone, now represented by a replica, at the junction of the A30 and the A325 Portsmouth road. There is a railway tunnel on the Ascot to Ash Vale line (LSWR, 1878) under the road junction.

The route of the A30 was turnpiked to this point in 1728 by the Bedfont & Bagshot Turnpike Trust, and the next section by the Bagshot & Basingstoke trust in 1737. Portland stone milestones were erected in 1743 and the series

from 20 to 30 miles from Hyde Park Corner survives in the borough.

The A325, turnpiked by the Winchester Upper District trust in 1753, has surviving milestones at 28, 29 and 30 miles from London.

### SH 02 BAGSHOT BRIDGE
SU 912 634 **CA**  ✳
Bridge taking the A30 over the River Bourne, reconstructed in concrete in 1925 when the Bagshot Bypass was made. The original bridge was built in 1768 and rebuilt in 1777. There is a stone **horse-trough** at SU 909 631.

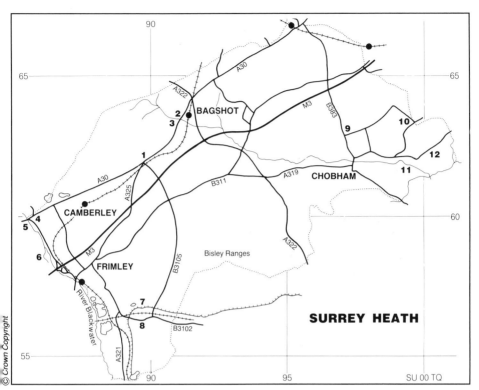

© Crown Copyright

**SURREY HEATH**

90    95    SU 00 TQ

90    65    65    60    55

## SH03 BAGSHOT WATERMILL

SU 908 631 **CA**    ✳

Three-storey brick corn mill with date plaque 1817, formerly with a 24 ft (7.5m) diameter overshot waterwheel. It was a sawmill by 1921 and now houses a joinery business. The mill pond survives and at one time fed a public water supply.

## SH04 CONCRETE ELEPHANT, CAMBERLEY

SU 855 600    ✳

On the A30 road. Figure of an elephant made from concrete pipes manufactured by the firm of Trollope & Colls, who occupied the site until 1967. It was made for the firm's float in the City of London Lord Mayor's Show in 1963 in which it was decorated as an Indian ceremonial elephant.

## SH05 YORK TOWN AND BLACKWATER GAS WORKS

SU 856 596    ✳

On the bank of the River Blackwater. Two gasholders survive.

## SH06 BLACKWATER VALLEY    ❏

Sand and gravel extraction was carried on from Aldershot in Hampshire to Yately in Berkshire between 1946 and 1983, resulting in many flooded pits. In 1979 the Blackwater Valley Team was formed, involving ten local authorities and other bodies, to reclaim the area for recreation, nature conservation and educational use.

Blackwater Bridge on the A30 [SU 854 598] was rebuilt in 1930.

Disused railway embankments on the north side of the main line were connecting spurs (closed 1964) to the Guildford to Reading line at Farnborough North and the Ascot to Ash Vale line at Frimley Junction [SU 884 565]. The line from the latter point to Ash Vale is single track.

## SH07 BASINGSTOKE CANAL CA    ❏

Mytchett Lake Road Bridge
[SU 892 543 ✳ ]

Narrow bridge over the Basingstoke Canal, probably original. The lake, together with Wharfenden Lake [SU 893 568] and Greatbottom Flash [SU 894 533], was probably a reservoir formed in a natural hollow when the canal was built.

Frimley Aqueduct, Deepcut [SU 893 565, ✳]

A four-arched aqueduct carries the Basingstoke Canal over the main railway line to Southampton. It replaced a two arched structure and was built to avoid disrupting traffic on

**37**

SH04 Concrete Elephant, Camberley
*Photo: C Shepheard*

the canal when the railway line was doubled to four tracks in 1900.

**Canal cutting**, Deepcut [SU 900 565, ✳]
A rebuilt road bridge at this point affords a view of the canal cutting (1793) which is nearly 1km long and up to about 20m deep. The canal was engineered by William Jessop and built by John Pinkerton 1788-94. The parallel Woking to Southampton railway cutting is close by.

## SH08 FRIMLEY WINDMILL
SU 896 562 **LSII**                                        ✳
A windmill on this site is mentioned in 14th century Court Rolls of Chertsey Abbey. The present structure, probably 18th century, was derelict by 1913-14 when part of the tower was incorporated into a private house.

## SH09 SILICA SAND MINES, BURROW HALL, CHOBHAM
SU 973 632
Fine silica sand occurring locally in the Bagshot beds was mined for glass making and for use in scouring powders. Known locally as 'treacle mines'. The site has been redeveloped for modern industrial use.

## SH10 GRACIOUS POND, CHOBHAM
SU 993 634                                                ✳
Created by Abbot Rutherwyke of Chertsey Abbey in the 14th century to serve as a fish pond and water supply.

## SH11 EMMETT'S MILL, CHOBHAM
SU 995 618 **LSII**                                        ✳
On the site of a 14th century mill on the Chertsey Abbey estate. The present 18th century structure forms one wing of a private house, with no surviving mill equipment.

## SH12 FAIROAKS AERODROME, CHOBHAM
TQ 001 622                                                ✳
First built during the Second World War, this now operates as a small private airfield. Current users include an airship advertising company.

SH07 Frimley aqueduct                                      *Photo: C Shepheard*

The easternmost district of Surrey extends from the suburban fringe of outer London to the largely agricultural Weald. Residential development in the north came with the SER line to Caterham, completed in 1855, and the line through Woldingham and Oxted to the south coast which came in the 1880s. Other developments peripheral to London included the Metropolitan Asylum (1869) and the Guards' Depot (1875) at Caterham, and Gardner's Pleasure Resort and Kenley Aerodrome, the sites of which are now in the London Borough of Croydon.

South of the Downs, along the Lower Greensand outcrop, is a line of settlements — Bletchingley, Godstone, Oxted and Limpsfield — linked by the A25 road. Godstone was a coaching stop on the route (the modern A22 to Eastbourne) through the Godstone gap.

Extractive industries have been of major importance and some remain active, in particular sandpits near Godstone and limeworks north of Oxted. Many old workings are used as landfill sites. Fuller's earth extraction has virtually ceased and proposals to open new pits at Godstone and Tandridge village were turned down in 1989. Old underground stone quarries form an extensive network in the Upper Greensand. Brickmaking on the Weald clay continues at South Godstone.

In the largely rural south-east corner of the county, Lingfield is known for its racecourse (1890) and there were interesting residential developments in the Victorian and Edwardian periods.

Numerous mill ponds occur on streams flowing into the River Eden, itself a tributary of the Medway. Some were associated with the iron industry but most with corn milling. The district has the only working water corn mill in Surrey, Coltsford mill near Oxted, and the oldest working windmill in Britain at Outwood.

## Ta 01 RAILWAY VIADUCT, KENLEY

TQ 337 593     ✳

On the east side of the A22 Godstone Road, a lattice girder viaduct on brick piers carries the joint LBSCR/SER Croydon to Oxted line (1884) across a large disused chalk pit which was worked from the early 18th century to the 1960s. There was formerly a cottage beneath the viaduct which was leased to quarry workers.

There is a 1950s gas holder on the British Gas site adjacent at TQ 337 592.

## Ta02 COAL TAX POSTS, WHYTELEAFE

TQ 340 581 LSII     ✳

There is a 4.3m (14ft) stone railway obelisk south of Whyteleafe station. There are standard cast iron posts in Whyteleafe Hill [TQ 338 583] and outside 376 Godstone Road [TQ 341 580]

## Ta03 OXTED RAILWAY TUNNEL

TQ 365 555 — 377 539     ✳

Tunnel through the North Downs, 2087m long. It was begun in 1865 by the Surrey and Sussex Junction Railway Company on the proposed line from Croydon to Brighton via East Grinstead (1884).

## Ta 04 OXTED CHALK PITS

TQ 38 54     ✳

Large chalk pits of the Oxted Greystone Lime Co are seen from the M25. There is an active limeworks (Tilcon Limited] west of Chalkpit Lane at TQ 383 543.

## Ta05 OXTED MILL

TQ 390 518 LS     ✳

Domesday mill site on a tributary of the River Eden, now occupied by an electrical components manufacturer. A two-storey brick-built corn mill with luccam, external undershot wheel and three pairs of stones was extended in 1893, the wheel enclosed and roller milling equipment added. A surviving Girard vertical shaft water turbine by Günter's of Oldham was probably installed at that time.

## Ta06 COLTSFORD MILL

TQ 397 505 LSII     ❏

On a Domesday mill site on the River Eden. The present 18th century corn mill is brick to the first floor with weatherboarding above, under a Mansard roof. It has 4 pairs of stones and a 5m (16ft) iron overshot waterwheel. It is **39** the only working watermill in Surrey, although not in commercial use. The pit floor is used as a restaurant.

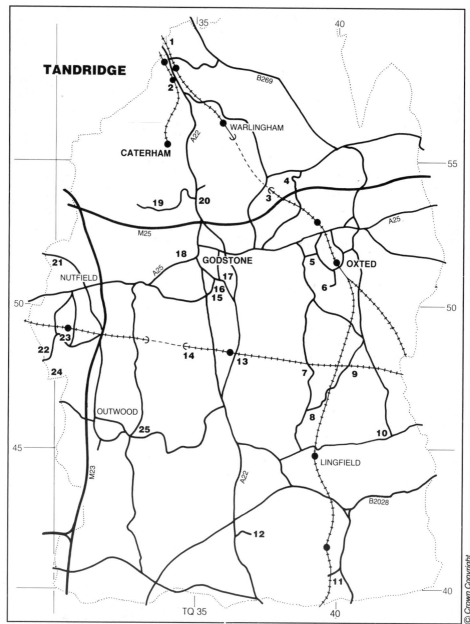

## Ta07 IRON GRAVE SLAB, CROWHURST CHURCH

TQ 391 475

Wealden iron grave slab over the tomb of Ann Forster (d.1591) set in the chancel floor of St George's Church. There is a **causeway** to the church from Crowhurst Place [TQ 386 464] built in 1631 by John Gainesford.

## Ta08 REDLAND BRICKS LIMITED, CROWHURST

TQ 393 465

Brickmaking ceased in 1979. A Staffordshire continuous kiln with 22 chambers remains but its central chimney stack has been taken down.

Ta04 Oxted lime kilns, early 20th century
*Photo: Roger Packham Collection*

### Ta09 OASTHOUSE, CROWHURST
TQ 402 474 ✳

Red brick oasthouse with tiled cone and wooden cowl at Oldhouse Farm, Caterfield Lane.

### Ta10 HAXTED MILL, EDENBRIDGE
TQ 419 455 **LSII** ❏

On the River Eden. Part of the building dates back to 1680 on earlier foundations. Corn milling ceased in 1944. The mill, with its external overshot waterwheel, has been restored and converted into a museum, with exhibits rescued from demolished mills in the south of England.

### Ta11 DORMANS PARK VIADUCT
TQ 398 402 ✳

Railway viaduct on the LBSCR line to East Grinstead (1884), by James Firbank. Built of lattice girders on brick piers. It carries the line over Cook's Pond, which is probably an early millpond. **Dormans Park** is a residential area begun in the 1880s by the Bellagio Estate Limited, which built bungalow residences as weekend retreats.

### Ta12 WOODCOCK HAMMER
TQ 369 419 ✳

Wealden iron forge site worked in association with Warren Furnace, Worth, Sussex [TQ 348 393]. It was established by 1561, closed by 1787 and the site was later reused for a wire mill and corn mill. The pond, known as Wire Mill Lake, is in water and the tail race remains.

### Ta13 LAGHAM MANOR, SOUTH GODSTONE
TQ 349 484 **LSII** ✳

Moated manor house with 18th century brewhouse, oasthouse and stables.

### TQ14 BRICKWORKS, SOUTH GODSTONE
TQ 349 484 ✳

The active brickworks of W T Lamb & Sons manufactures stock bricks. Waste fuel is added to the clay to produce mottled red bricks containing black clinker. Work is labour intensive, the moulded bricks being knocked out by hand, and firing is in eight intermittent up-draught or **Scotch kilns**, now fired by gas. The works has been in the Lamb family for some 80 years.

Ta09 Oast house, Crowhurst
*Photo: C Shepheard*

**41**

### Ta15 SECOND WORLD WAR ROAD BLOCKS, ENTERDENT

TQ 355 505         ✳

Concrete cylinders along the road over Tilburstowhill Common.

### Ta16 MILESTONE, B2236

TQ 357 508         ✳

Milestone on south side of the old A22 road, XX miles from Westminster Bridge and XXI miles from the Standard in Cornhill. It was originally on the earlier route of the turnpike along Tilburstow Hill Road.

### Ta17 LEIGH MILL, GODSTONE

TQ 361 509 **LSII**         ✳

A Domesday mill site on the Gibbs Brook. From the late 16th century to 1635 it was used for gunpowder manufacture by John and Robert Evelyn, sons of George Evelyn. The family was also active at Tolworth (EE 12) and Wotton (MV 02). The mill later reverted to corn milling. The present 18th century brick and weatherboarded building was converted into a private house after milling ceased in 1934 but the waterwheel and pit machinery remain. The wheel is visible in winter from the Greensand Way footpath.

### Ta18 SAND PITS, GODSTONE   ✳

The village of Godstone is much undermined with old workings for silver sand. Open-cast workings include the active pit at North Park Farm [TQ 340 525] and a wildlife sanctuary west of the village [TQ 345 517].

### Ta19 WATER TOWER, GRAVELLY HILL

TQ 337 533         ✳

Red brick East Surrey Water Company tower, built in 1897.

### Ta20 GODSTONE STONE MINES

TQ 347 532--TQ 360 532

Underground firestone quarries in the Upper Greensand at Godstone Hill were reopened in the 19th century for hearthstone mining which continued to 1947. Other mines were opened and there are about ten entrances in the area. Some galleries were later used for mushroom growing.

### Ta21 FULLER'S EARTH WORKINGS, NUTFIELD

The area has been extensively worked over a long period and several pits have been worked out in recent years. Fuller's earth deposits were found in the cutting for the M23 motorway [TQ 315 517] in 1972 and pits were subsequently opened east of Nutfield church. These have been worked out and restored to meadowland. At Nutfield village, a nature reserve was established in 1988 following the demolition of the Park Works processing plant [TQ 305 506]. Features include shallow settling pits and a pond formed in a deep excavation at the north end at TQ 301 514.

### Ta22 KINGS MILL, SOUTH NUTFIELD

TQ 299 489 **LSII**         ✳

Brick and weatherboarded corn mill with fine Mansard roof, converted into offices.

### Ta23 ACID WORKS SITE, SOUTH NUTFIELD

TQ 300 490

Now residential. There was a brickworks c1871 to the First World War, then National Reclaimers Ltd recovered wax from papier mache jam pots returned from the battle front to South Nutfield station. The wax was recycled by the British Wax Refining Co Ltd (RB 18). The Nutfield Manufacturing Co was established in 1925 by James Wilkinson of Sheffield to manufacture hydrofluoric acid. Later products included permanent hair wave preparations, battery acid, cleaning chemicals and solvents. The firm became part of RTZ Borax in the 1960s. The works closed in 1984.

### Ta24 REDHILL AERODROME

TQ 297 480         ✳

Established in 1934 and used for training Imperial Airways engineers. Redhill Flying Club and an RAF training school were formed in 1937.

The aerodrome expanded and held a major air display just before the outbreak of war in 1939, when it became an RAF fighter base. There are 'pillbox' gun emplacements on the perimeter. Now used by Bristow Helicopters Ltd.

### Ta25 OUTWOOD WINDMILL

TQ 328 456 **LS1**         ❑

*Also see photograph on page 1*

Post mill built in 1665, the oldest working windmill in the country. It has been restored by its present owners Mr G and Mr R Thomas who work the mill on open days in the summer months. An adjacent smock mill, built c1880, was blown down in 1960 and cleared away.

Ta25 Outwood post mill     *Photo: C Shepheard*

The modern borough is named after Waverley Abbey [SU 868 453], a Cistercian foundation of 1128. The abbey played a major role in developing the woollen industry. Its influence can also be seen in a series of distinctive stone arch bridges on the River Wey.

Traces of the Wealden iron industry can be seen in the Haslemere and Thursley areas. However only excavated features remain of the important forest glass industry which prospered around Chiddingfold from the 14th to 16th centuries.

There are four main urban centres: Farnham, Godalming, Haslemere and Cranleigh.

Farnham, with its medieval castle, the residence of the Bishops of Winchester, was a centre of hop growing and allied industries. There is an active pottery at Wrecclesham and there are sandpits in the Lower Greensand.

Godalming was a staging post on the London to Portsmouth road and a trading centre at the head of the Godalming Navigation which opened in 1763. The town was associated with the woollen industry, which did not entirely die out when the trade declined in the 17th century, and with tanning which continued until the early 1950s. Other industries included brewing, corn milling, the quarrying of Bargate building stone and papermaking. Framework knitting was introduced from London in the 17th century. The last knitwear firm in Godalming, Alan Paine Limited, is closing in 1990 and moving its manufacturing plant to its secondary factory in South Wales. The knitwear industry in the region is now represented only by a small factory in Guildford which manufactures cricket sweaters.

Haslemere and Cranleigh in the south are prosperous residential areas. Haslemere had several corn mills which variously changed to minor textile manufactures and papermaking. In the 20th century it has been the home of the Dolmetsch family, promoters of early music and musical instrument makers. The heathland to the west was known for the manufacture of birch and hazel

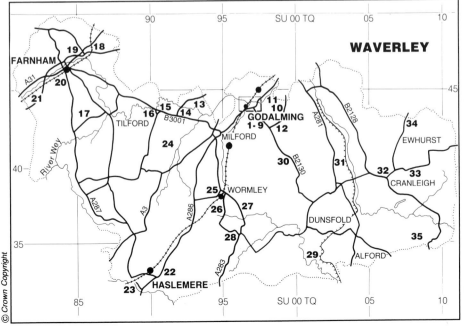

brooms. There are active brick and tile works on the Weald clay in the Cranleigh area and at Hambledon.

Some modern industry exists amid rural surroundings. Weyburn-Bartel manufacture vehicle camshafts near Elstead and the Second World War airfield at Dunsfold is still used as a test-centre for military aircraft.

## Wa01 GODALMING MUSEUM
SU 968 438  **CA**                                  ❏

Opposite the Pepperpot, the Old Market Hall built in 1814. Displays on local industries include a stocking frame and a model of the water turbine from Catteshall Mill (Wa 07, 11).

## Wa02 BUTCHER'S SHOP,
## 137 HIGH STREET, GODALMING
SU 967 438  **CA**                                  ✳

Art Deco style shop front in deep blue tiles with ornamental cows' heads at the corners. Used as Stovold's dairy shop 1928-89 and refitted 1989-90.

## Wa03 FRAMESHOP,
## 22 MINT STREET, GODALMING.
SU 967 438  **CA**                                  ✳

A 3-storey framework knitter's workshop was built at the rear of an altered 16th century house in the late 18th century. This, with its long upper window now blocked, can be viewed from the steps of the Friends' Meeting House in Mill Lane. The top storey was subsequently extended over the front of the house, which also has a long window on the second floor.

## Wa04 HATCH MILL, MILL LANE, GODALMING
SU 966 438  **LSII, CA**                            ✳

Weather-boarded corn mill with distinctive luccam, closed in 1965 and now occupied by various businesses. A water turbine by Gilbert Gilkes & Gordon of Kendal (1940) can be seen above the former water wheel pit.

## Wa05 HOSIERY FACTORY, MILL LANE, GODALMING
SU 966 438                                          ✳

Purpose-built c1870 by Allen & Solly, a Nottingham firm which employed domestic labour in the Midlands and opened its first factory in Godalming in 1860. Fine underclothing was made for export. The firm moved its factory operation to Nottingham in 1888.

Godalming railway station (1859) is nearby.

## Wa06 PHILLIPS MEMORIAL, GODALMING
SU 968 440  **CA**                                  ❏

Memorial to Jack Phillips of Farncombe, wireless operator on the Titanic which sank in 1912. The brick cloister (1913) was designed by Hugh

Thackeray Turner and the gardens by Gertrude Jekyll, who lived at Munstead Wood.

## Wa07 WESTBROOK MILL, GODALMING
SU 967 443          *See also photograph on page 4*

An early mill site formerly used by various industries including corn milling, fulling, paper making, flock making, tanning and pharmaceuticals and occupied since 1981 by the consulting engineers Kennedy & Donkin.

Electricity for the world's first public **electric street lighting** was generated on the site in 1881. The system used Siemens generators powered by a waterwheel and arc lights and incandescent lights in the town. It was not an economic success and was discontinued in 1884. No plant survives but the outlet hole can be seen of a turbine used to generate electricity for the tannery of R & J Pullman Ltd in 1903 [SU 964 443]. The town did not provide electricity again until about 1910.

A large **Fourneyron-MacAdam water turbine SC** is stored on the site. It was made by MacAdam Brothers, Belfast and installed at

Wa05 Allen & Solly hosiery factory, Godalming
*Photo: G M Crocker*

MacAdam-Fourneyron
water turbine from Catteshall
Mill.
Drawing: Copyright Neil Cossons 1987

A: bearing beam
B: main support beams
C: crown wheel
D: pinion takes power to
machinery
E: stator tube
F: rotor shaft
G: control gate raised or lowered
to vary power output
H: fixed guide vanes of stator
inside rotor
J: vaned rotor outside stator turns
shaft

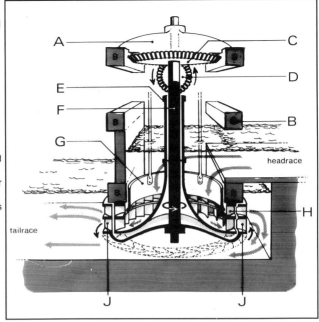

Catteshall Mill (Wa 11) by Messrs Spicer in 1869 to drive paper making machinery mechanically. A model is held by Godalming Museum (Wa01).

## Wa08 RAILWAY SLEEPER BLOCKS, CHALK ROAD, GODALMING
SU 974 444 ✳

Granite blocks with pairs of holes for chairs form a low wall near the site of the first Godalming LSWR station (1849) which has been redeveloped. Others occur at Tongham [SU 886 491] on the former Guildford to Farnham line (closed 1937).

## Wa09 GODALMING WHARF
SU 975 440 ✳

Limit of the Godalming Navigation (opened 1763). Cargoes to London included timber, planks, hoops, bark, flour and manufactured iron. Commercial traffic ceased in 1925 and the area has been redeveloped.

## Wa10 HYDRAULIC RAM, CATTESHALL LANE
SU 984 442 ✳

Installed in the 1920s by John Blake Ltd of Accrington, probably for the gardens of Catteshall Manor. The ram can be seen working through a glass panel, although the water now goes to waste. It features on the inn sign of *The Ram* cider house opposite.

## Wa11 CATTESHALL MILL
SU 983 443 ✳

An early mill site previously used for corn milling, fulling, paper making and engineering and foundry work, and now partly redeveloped. A MacAdam-Fourneyron **water turbine** was removed to Westbrook (Wa 07) in 1981. The head of water is also used by Catteshall lock [SU 981 444] on the **Godalming Navigation**. Farncombe boathouse is adjacent to the mill.

## Wa12 MUNSTEAD WATER TOWER, GODALMING
SU 987 427 **LSII** ✳

An imposing brick water tower built in 1898, now disused.

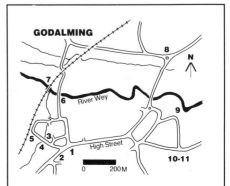

### Wa13 DOVECOTES, PEPER HAROW
SU 93 44 **LSII**   ✳
Octagonal dovecote at Peper Harow House [SU 936 441], built in 1763, . and red brick dovecote at the nearby farm [SU 934 442], built in 1775.

### Wa14 MEDIEVAL BRIDGES, RIVER WEY
**SC, LSII**   ✳
Several Bargate rubble bridges, probably 13th century, span the Wey between Farnham and Guildford. Distinctive downstream buttresses are semi-circular in plan. Examples are Somerset Bridge [SU 922 439], Elstead Bridge [SU 905 438, **CA**], two bridges at Tilford [SU 872 435, **CA**] and two at Eashing (Gu 24).

### Wa15 ELSTEAD FORGE
SU 907 437 **CA**   ✳
A forge by the village green has the date 1686 carved in stone. The post office adjacent was the original blacksmith's cottage.

### Wa16 ELSTEAD MILL
SU 903 438 **LSII★, CA**   ❑
Probably a Domesday mill site. The present 18th century brick building is occupied by a restaurant from which a 16 ft (5m) diameter breast-shot waterwheel can be seen.
Corn milling ceased in the early 19th century. The mill was occupied by Appleton's **worsted braid and small ware manufactory** 1830s-1880s. From 1913 the water wheel was used to generate electricity for the mill house.
A Second World War 'pillbox' adjacent is disguised as a summer house.

### Wa17 OLD KILN MUSEUM, REEDS ROAD, TILFORD
SU 858 433   ❑
Private open-air museum of rural life containing collections of farm machinery and various craft workshops. It houses the reserve collection of the Museum of English Rural Life, Reading and the gantry crane from the **Thames Ditton statue foundry** (see Elmbridge). Special events are held during the open season.

### Wa18 HOP KILNS, BADSHOT LEA FARM
SU 864 480 **LSII**   ✳
19th century kiln block, used as a farm store until the 1960s and converted into a community centre in the 1980s.

### Wa19 BOURNE MILL, FARNHAM
SU 853 474 **LSII**   ❑
A beautiful mellow six-storey building with a loft, 17th century and later, occupied by antique businesses. No machinery survives.

### Wa20 FARNHAM MALTINGS
SU 841 466 **LSII, CA**   ❑
In mellow red brick, mostly 19th century but incorporating parts of an earlier brewery and tannery. Occupied by Courages 1920 -1956. Demolition was proposed in 1968 but the building was bought for the town by public subscription and later, converted for community use.

### Wa21 FARNHAM POTTERIES, POTTERY LANE, WRECCLESHAM
SU 824 446   ✳
Pottery on Gault Clay, established in 1873 by Absalom Harris and still run by the Harris family in the original buildings. It specialises in garden pottery and was formerly known for copper-glazed green ware.

### Wa22 HASLEMERE MUSEUM   ❑
SU 906 331 **LSII, CA**
Specialises in natural history but also contains displays on Wealden iron and glass and holds a local paper maker's mould (1812) and the toll board from Winter-

Wa18 Elliott's patent hop bagging machine in use in Badshot Farm Kiln, c1890
*Photo: Chris Shepheard Collection*

ton toll house, used c1824-71 (Wa 27).

## Wa23 SICKLE MILL, HASLEMERE

SU 888 326 **LSII**  ✳

Probably mid 18th century, possibly on an earlier iron working site. It was a paper mill from the 1730s to the 1860s and drying sheds can still be distinguished. An important set of diaries survives of the papermaker James Simmons, who also ran two other papermills in the district, now demolished.

The mill was later used in conjunction with Elstead Mill (Wa 16) for the manufacture of braid and trimmings. It was sold to the local authority in the 1920s and became a council depot. Its future is under review.

## Wa24 WEALDEN IRON SITES, THURSLEY

SU 91 40  ✳

Three forge sites with surviving hammer ponds and bays, on streams flowing into Warren Mere, comprise Upper [SU 916 403] and Lower [SU 916 408] sites on the westerly stream and Horsebane forge [SU 920 406] on the easterly stream. First recorded in 1608. One site, probably Lower forge, was still active in 1767 but by 1805 was occupied by a silk crape mill. A house on the site is called Silkmill Cottage. There is also an iron furnace site at Witley Park [SU 927 374].

Shallow pits, probably for the extraction of ironstone, can be seen on the south-east side of the A3 road at SU 916 400.

## Wa25 GAS RETORT HOUSE, WITLEY

SU 949 385  ■

A small, single storey brick building in the grounds of King Edward's School [**LSII**]. Gas was produced for lighting and cooking. The plant and gas holder were removed 1922-5 but plans, by Thomas Rider & Son of London, 1878, are preserved in the school archive.

## Wa26 WALKING STICK FACTORY, WORMLEY

SU 949 375  ✳

Active works of G Cooper & Sons which has been making walking sticks for over 100 years. Some of the wood is obtained locally and some is imported from many parts of the world. Modern walking aids are also made to the firm's own designs. Half the production is exported, in particular, shepherds' crooks to New Zealand.

## Wa27 WINTERTON TOLLHOUSE, CHIDDINGFOLD

SU 960 372  ✳

Brick and stone 2-storey tollhouse on the Petworth road. The half-hexagonal end has space for the tollboard, held by Haslemere Museum (Wa 22).

## Wa28 SMITHY, CHIDDINGFOLD

SU 961 354 **LSII, CA**  ✳

Recorded as a forge site since the 13th century. The last horse was shod in 1952. The present building is owned by the Society for the Protection of Ancient Buildings and is occupied by a craftsman blacksmith.

Chiddingfold Church nearby [SU 960 354] has a window (1916) made up of 427 fragments (224 coloured) of **Wealden glass**. One white piece has been dated not later than 1325 and much of the rest 1425-1550.

## Wa29 KNIGHTON'S GLASS FURNACE, ALFOLD

TQ 017 341  ✳

On a Forest Trail remains can be seen of a two-chamber furnace for annealing crown sheets of glass. The site, active c1550, was excavated by the Surrey Archaeological Society 1965-73.

Nearby are decayed locks of the **Wey & Arun Canal** and the fine canal agent's house at TQ 017 338.

The grave of Jean Carré, a French immigrant glass maker (d. 1572) is reputed to be under a marble slab near the war memorial at St Nicholas Church, Alfold [TQ 037 340].

## Wa30 TOLL HOUSE AND MILE POST, HASCOMBE

SU 999 401  ✳

Single storey brick toll house, 1826, on the turnpike road (now the B2130) which linked Godalming with the Guildford to Horsham road. The cast iron mile post nearby is one of a series of six by Williams & Filmer of Guildford. These have been restored by Surrey County Council in conjunction with local organisations.

## Wa31 ROWLY LOCK, WEY & ARUN CANAL

TQ 035 401  ✳

Lock 17, restored by the Wey & Arun Canal Trust 1982-6.

## Wa32 TURNPIKE OBELISK, CRANLEIGH

TQ 061 391 **LSII, CA**  ✳

7.5m sandstone column with iron direction and mileage plates cast by the local blacksmith, T Champion. It is said to have been erected in 1794 and if this is correct it predates the turnpike Act (1818).

## Wa33 SWALLOW'S TILE WORKS, CRANLEIGH

TQ 076 395  ✳

Brookhurst Brick and Tile Works (established 1894) still operates, specialising in hand-made, sand-faced tiles with a rough weathered appearance and variations in colour.

**47**

## Wa 34 EWHURST WINDMILL

TQ 078 427

A 4-storey brick tower mill of 1840, which replaced a postmill of 1640, was converted into a summer residence in 1901. The framework of the sweeps survives. The ogee cap contains the wooden brake wheel on a cast iron windshaft.

## Wa 35 BAYNARDS RAILWAY STATION

TQ 076 351

On the disused line of the Horsham & Guildford Direct Railway Company (incorporated into the LBSCR) which operated 1865-1965.

The route now forms part of the Downs Link footpath. The station was built as part of an agreement with the landowner, Lord Thurlow, who was granted a daily carriage to London by the Company. It served a local brickworks and the Fuller's earth works of F W Berk Ltd. It is in private hands and has been restored to its original condition and LBSCR colours. The goods shed retains a LBSCR crane, now unique.

Wa33 Swallow's tile works, Cranleigh

*Drawing: R Oliver*

The original village on the River Wey is now known as Old Woking, as distinct from the modern town which grew up around the railway. A station was opened on Woking Common by the London & Southampton Railway Company (later the London & South Western) in 1838. The railway line ran close to the Basingstoke Canal which was completed in 1794 and fully opened in 1796. However development of the town did not begin until 1852 when the London Necropolis & National Mausoleum Company was authorised by Parliament to purchase the common. The plan was for a vast cemetery served by a special railway service from Waterloo. Burials in London graveyards had been banned in 1850 and the need for space was acute. The Bill was passed despite doubts about the Company's intentions, and indeed only 400 acres were ever used for the cemetery, the remaining 1,868 being later sold for residential and other use at considerable profit.

The light soils of the Bagshot and Bracklesham beds have long been used for nursery gardening. Numerous firms operated in the 19th century, some of which have continued to the present day, including Waterer's, Slocock's, and Jackman's who bred the famous *Clematis Jackmanni*.

Some of the nurserymen also engaged in brickmaking, using locally occurring clays. A large local demand for bricks was created by the building of locks and bridges on the canal and later by the building of houses and the large institutions of which Woking had a concentration. These included the Invalid Convict Prison (1859) which later became the Inkerman Barracks, the Royal Dramatic College (Wk 02), the Surrey County Pauper Lunatic Asylum (1866) which became Brookwood Hospital, and the London & South Western Railway Servants' Orphanage (1909).

As the town grew, various industries were established including soap manufacture, printing and engineering.

Proximity to London has led to continued residential expansion. West Byfleet grew up around a new LSWR main line station, built on common land in 1887 [TQ 042 611]. More recently the residential and industrial development of Goldsworth Park took place in the 1970s on land sold by Slocock's nurseries. Redevelopment of the town centre has been carried out in recent years and is continuing.

## Wk01 WOKING STATION
TQ 006 587 ❏
The original Woking Common Station was opened in 1838.

The last rebuild was in 1937. The station faces south, the direction from which most travellers initially came, but this side was reserved by the Necropolis Company for high class residential building and the town centre grew up behind the station.

All road routes through the town centre pass under the railway at Victoria Arch [TQ 004 586], known as the Railway Arch until 1898, which was widened in 1906-7.

The Sovereigns public house [TQ 005 584] in Guildford Road was formerly the Railway Hotel, built in 1840 at the junction of several tracks across the common, when the station was the railhead for the region.

## Wk02 JAMES WALKER LIMITED, LION WORKS
TQ 017 592 ✳
The present Lion Works occupies the site of the Royal Dramatic College, a home for retired actors and actresses, built in 1860-2. The company's boardroom occupies the original Elizabethan style Central Hall. The College closed for financial reasons in 1877 and was acquired by Dr Gottlieb Wilhelm Leitner, a Hungarian orientalist who established the Oriental Institute in the former college buildings and also founded the nearby Shah Jehan Mosque [TQ 015 592, **LS**] in 1889. After Leitner's death, parts of the 10 acre site were occupied from 1910 to 1918 by the Electrical Accumulator Supply Company, established in the town 1894, and from 1914 to 1924 by Martinsyde Aircraft Limited, founded by H P Martin and G H Handyside who built the first plane at Brooklands (El 01).

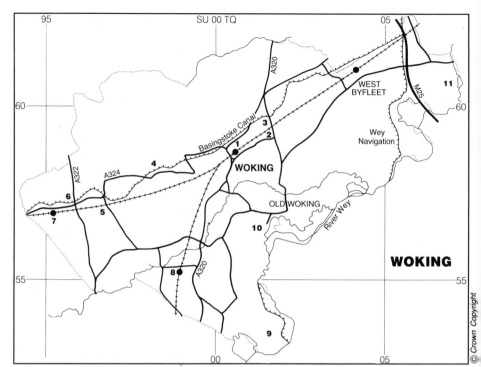

James Walker Ltd manufactures packings, seals and gaskets. The surviving chimney stack was associated with coal fired boilers which formerly provided processed steam for vulcanising. The firm was established in east London in 1882 and moved to Woking in 1926. It has several other factories in Britain and abroad and is Woking's largest employer with over 900 workers at three establishments in the town.

### Wk03 MONUMENT BRIDGE, BASINGSTOKE CANAL

TQ 016 597 **CA** ✳

Restoration of the canal is nearing completion in 1990, ending with the length east of Monument Bridge. The present bridge dates from the late 1930s. There are modern trading estates on the south side of the canal. Following the towpath westwards along the south bank, there is winding gear by Tangye of Birmingham near the bridge. Two **gas holders** are seen at Woking gas works. Coal was delivered there by barge until 1936 and timber to Spanton's timber wharf until 1949. There is an open space on the site of the timber yards (demolished 1972). Chertsey Road Bridge [TQ 010 594] was rebuilt in the 1920s and Chobham Road Bridge [TQ 006 591] in 1913. Arthur's Bridge [SU 995 586] is original but was repaired in the 1920s.

**50**

### Wk04 GOLDSWORTH LOCKS, BASINGSTOKE CANAL

SU 980 584—SU 980 580 **CA** ✳

Features include, from east to west, the original brick arch Goldsworth Bridge and locks 7-9, Woodend Bridge (original) and St John's Bridge, which was rebuilt as an iron girder bridge in 1899. This is also known as Kiln Bridge, a reference to the brick industry which last operated in 1942.

### Wk05 RAILWAY ARCH, BLACKHORSE ROAD

SU 967 572 ✳

An original long, narrow railway arch under the Woking to Southampton line. The road through the arch crosses the canal at Hermitage Bridge (rebuilt 1906) and approaches **Brookwood Hospital**, formerly the asylum.

### Wk06 BROOKWOOD LOCKS, BASINGSTOKE CANAL

SU 958 572—SU 954572 **CA** ✳

A flight of three locks, numbers 12-14, above Brookwood road bridge (rebuilt 1914).

### Wk07 BROOKWOOD STATION AND CEMETERY

SU 952 569 ❏

A branch line from 'Necropolis Junction' into Brookwood Cemetery was opened in 1854 to convey funeral parties from London Waterloo.

There were two stations, one for Anglicans and one for others. Only the platforms and line of the track can now be distinguished.

The main line station was opened in 1864 on land donated by the Necropolis Company. It was enlarged in 1890 when the Bisley Branch Line was added to serve the National Rifle Association's ranges [SU 93 58]. In 1952 the Bisley line closed and the track was lifted.

## Wk08 WORPLESDON STATION

SU 989 553 ☐

Opened in 1883. The **Owen Stone Company** manufactured artificial stone just south of the station from 1897 to 1910 when it was discovered that the product crumbled. The cutting for the works siding is still visible.

## Wk09 SUTTON PLACE

TQ 013 536 **LSI** ■

Home of Sir Richard Weston, promoter of the Wey Navigation. An agricultural improver, he earlier cut an irrigation channel from the river at Stoke, where he also built a paper mill (Gu 15), to fields near Sutton Place and built an experimental pound lock at Stoke to control the water level.

The house, one of the finest of its period, was built by an earlier Sir Richard Weston c1523-5.

It was the home of the oil magnate Paul Getty (d.1976), is in private hands and has been closed in recent years.

## Wk10 UNWIN'S PRINTING WORKS, OLD WOKING

TQ 016 565

Active printing works of Unwin Brothers' Gresham Press, now part of the Staples Printing Group. The works occupies the premises of a former paper mill (1840-1895) on an early mill site on the River Wey. Unwin's moved here when their works at Chilworth in the parish of St Martha's (Gu 28) burned down in 1895 and retained the name 'St Martha's Printing Works'. Several water turbines were used of which engineering drawings survive.

## Wk11 BYFLEET MILL

TQ 073 607 **LSII★** ■

18th century weatherboarded corn mill on Domesday mill site, closed c1930 in connection with flood prevention; converted to residential use with no public access. A papermill (1673) was leased from 1690 by the Company of White Papermakers of England. In the 18th century, it was an iron and brass mill associated with the Bristol Company of Wiredrawers.

**51**

Wk04 Lock 7 and Goldsworth Bridge, Basingstoke Canal, in 1985     *Photo: Clive Durley*

# BIBLIOGRAPHY

G R Baker    *A guide to the industrial archaeology of Elmbridge.* Guildford, SIHG, 1990

D A Bayliss    *Retracing the first public railway.* Croydon, Living History Publications, 1981

P Brandon    *A history of Surrey.* Chichester, Phillimore, 1977

P Brandon    Land, technology and water management in the Tillingbourne Valley. *Southern History,* 6 (1984), 75-103

Brit. Assoc. for the Advancem't of Science.    *The Surrey Countryside.* Guildford, University of Surrey, 1975

H Cleere & D Crossley    *The iron industry of the Weald.* Leicester, Leicester University Press, 1985

A Crocker    The paper mills of Surrey. *Surrey History,* 4 no 1 (1989), 49-62

G Crocker    The Godalming framework knitting industry. *Surrey History,* 4 no 1 (1989), 2-16

G Crocker: compiled by    *Gunpowder Mills Survey,* London, SPAB, 1988

K G Farries & M T Mason    *The windmills of Surrey and inner London.* London, Charles Skilton, 1966

A J Haselfoot    *The Batsford guide to the industrial archaeology of South East England.* London, Batsford, 1978

F Haveron    *The Brilliant Ray* Godalming, Godalming Electricity Centenary Celebrations Committee, 1981

F Haveron    *A guide to the industrial archaeology of Waverley.* Guildford, SIHG, 1985

J Hillier    *Old Surrey water-mills.* London, Skeffington, 1951

T Holmes    *The semaphore.* Ilfracombe, Stockwell, 1983

G H Kenyon    *The glass industry of the Weald.* Leicester, Leicester University Press, 1967

C F Dendy Marshall    *A history of the southern railway.* London, Ian Allan, new ed 1982

G A Payne    *Surrey industrial archaeology.* Chichester, Phillimore, 1977

J F Potter    Ironworking in the vicinity of Weybridge, Surrey. *Industrial Archaeology Review,* 6 (1982), 211-223

P W Sowan    Firestone and hearthstone mines in the Upper Greensand of East Surrey. *Proc. Geologists' Assoc.* 86 (1975) 571-591

D Stidder    *The industrial archaeology of Reigate and Banstead District.* Guildford, SIHG, 1979

E Straker    *Wealden iron.* 1931, reprint Newton Abbot, David & Charles, 1969

D J Turner    *Surrey* (Ordnance Survey Historical Guides). London, George Philip, 1988

Victoria County History of Surrey    Volume 2. London, Constable, 1905

P A L Vine    *London's lost route to Basingstoke.* Newton Abbot, David & Charles, 1968

P A L Vine    *London's lost route to the sea.* 2nd ed Newton Abbot, David & Charles, 1986

H P White    *A regional history of the railways of Great Britain,* Volume 2, Southern England. New York, Augustus M Kelley, 1970

G Wilson    *The old telegraphs.* Chichester, Phillimore, 1976

# RECORD OFFICES, LIBRARIES & MUSEUMS

Surrey Record Office, County Hall, Penrhyn Road, Kingston upon Thames

Guildford Muniment Room, Castle Arch, Guildford

Surrey Local Studies Library, County Library, North Street, Guildford

**MUSEUMS**

The following museums are of interest, in addition to those included in the gazetteer of sites:

East Surrey Museum, 1 Stafford Road, Caterham (Ta) Surrey Heath Museum, Knoll Road. Camberley (SH)

Farnham Museum, 38 West Street, Farnham (Wa) Spelthorne Museum, Market Square, Staines (Sp)

Guildford Museum, Castle Arch, Guildford (Gu) Weybridge Museum, Church Street, Weybridge (El).

COVER ILLUSTRATIONS: *Front cover:* Gu02 Treadwheel crane, Guildford *Drawing: P Watkins*
*Back cover:* MV22 Betchworth lime kilns *Photo: C Shepheard*